D1273350

Girl with a Pen

GIRL WITH A PEN

Charlotte Brontë

BY ELISABETH KYLE

HOLT, RINEHART AND WINSTON

NEW YORK · CHICAGO · SAN FRANCISCO

I wish to thank Mr. Donald Hopewell, M.A., LL.B., the President of the Brontë Society, for reading my book and for invaluable help and advice.

Published simultaneously in Canada by Holt, Rinehart and Winston of Canada. Library of Congress Catalog Card Number: 64-14576. Printed in the United States of America. 95103-0114.
Published, March, 1964
Second Printing, February, 1965
Third Printing, July, 1965

CONTENTS

PART ONE 1833–1841

Charlotte at Home

CHAPTER *One*

"Have you remembered the pincushion, Charlotte?"

"No, Aunt Branwell. That is—I would have thought of it presently."

"I have thought of it now."

Miss Branwell stood on the threshold of Charlotte's room and handed a pincushion to her niece. Charlotte laid the pincushion on the dressing table which had been cleared of her own possessions. She had already laid out the toilet set which had belonged to her dead mother, in honor of Ellen. She had polished the silver backs of the brushes until they shone. She bent over them a moment to be sure no specks remained, then glanced at herself in the glass, just to see if she was tidy. Although Charlotte was now grown-up and had left school, she was so tiny she had to stand on tiptoe.

And what did she see? Mouse-brown hair parted in the middle and brushed smooth as silk; a large forehead and two very bright eyes; a bumpy nose and a badly shaped mouth. No beauty certainly, except for the eyes which changed color like amber jewels, brilliant as lamps when lit up by thought or feeling. Many visitors to Haworth

Parsonage thought Charlotte Brontë was plain, until her eyes looked full into theirs. Then they generally revised their opinion.

Charlotte herself didn't realize this. She thought she was ugly. She sighed, then glancing once more at the silver brushes and her own reflection above them, said slowly, "Ellen is very pretty. Her own dressing table at 'The Rydings' has a pink silk cover with muslin festoons."

"I hope having a wealthy schoolfellow to visit you won't lead to foolish discontent," said Aunt Branwell as she turned away and went back across the landing toward her own room.

A spark of fire lit up Charlotte's eyes. Her wide, rather crooked mouth set firmly in determination not to answer back. Then it softened again as her young sister Anne stole into the room. Anne was still at her lessons, taught by Charlotte who also taught Emily; though Emily, the second of the three sisters, was only two years younger than herself.

Anne had a vase of flowers in her hand. She was much prettier than Charlotte, and the gentlest of them all. The vase contained wild harebells brought from the moors. She set it gently down on the dressing table, and the harebells nodded toward their own reflections in the looking glass opposite.

"I'm glad you thought of putting out Mama's brushes," she said approvingly, adding, "They look very handsome, don't they?"

In actual fact they were now rather thin and battered. But to the three girls who lived in this bleak parsonage on the Yorkshire Moors, their dead mother's toilet set represented the acme of elegance. Charlotte being the eldest, had been allowed to own it. But the brushes, the comb, the slim little buttonhook had lived so long in their satin-lined case she had almost forgotten what they looked like until today when she put them out in honor of Ellen.

Anne's eyes fell on the plain floor boards, scrubbed to whiteness but uncovered and hard. "Branwell says 'The Rydings' has rich carpets in every room. He saw them that time you stayed there and he went to escort you home."

Charlotte remembered those thick Turkey carpets and felt a slight twinge of shame. Suppressing it firmly she said, "I've told Ellen about Papa's horror of fire. I've warned her she'll have to do without a carpet, and curtains, too."

Anne said gently, "Then I suppose she will be sensible enough to bring warm bedroom slippers."

There was no guest room at the parsonage. Anne shared this room with Charlotte, but was going to sleep with Aunt Branwell so as to let Ellen Nussey take her place. Only Emily had a room to herself; such a tiny slip of a room nobody could possibly share it with her.

"Where *is* Emily?" Charlotte asked.

"Out on the moors as usual."

Charlotte frowned slightly. "I hope she'll be back in time to welcome Ellen. It's only polite."

"You know what Emily is," said Anne.

After Anne had gone, Charlotte went over to the window and stood there a few minutes. She was trying to calm herself. It was so very unusual for this household to have any visitors at all; especially such a visitor as Ellen Nussey, who belonged to quite a different world. Ellen's father was a rich man. She was accustomed to every sort of comfort at home. Charlotte herself had tasted that comfort when she paid her visit to the Nusseys a little while ago.

What would Ellen think of their bleak, simple Yorkshire ways here? It does not signify what she thinks, Charlotte told herself immediately. She is coming here to see me; not to see how we live.

The window was open and though it looked to the back of the house and the moors beyond, she could hear suddenly the clip-clop of horses' hoofs approaching the front. She ran out of the room hastily and downstairs. The front door stood open, too. She could see her brother Branwell down at the gate already. Then he vanished through it, and she ran after him as the sound of carriage wheels stopped.

By the time she reached the gate herself, Branwell had helped Ellen out of the carriage. Ellen was looking down, so for the moment she didn't see Charlotte approach. When she raised her head, Charlotte saw the same lovely face, the same gentle expression she knew so well. And the same warm heart, too, for Ellen's arms were around her school friend's neck in a moment.

They walked slowly toward the house while Branwell was helping the coachman to fetch down Ellen's box. Now Mr. Brontë himself stood on the doorstep to welcome Charlotte's friend. This was a special honor as he did not often leave the seclusion of his study. Tall and majestic, with a white neckcloth folded under his chin, he waited for her to approach.

Ellen curtseyed. He bowed.

"Welcome, Miss Nussey," he said. "I bid you welcome for my daughter's sake as well as your own."

Then, to Ellen's astonishment, he turned back abruptly, stalked through the hall toward the study, and disappeared. Charlotte pulled her friend hastily toward the staircase, whispering, "You mustn't mind Papa. He lives very much by himself. In coming out of his room to greet you he paid you a most unusual compliment."

Ellen nodded and dimpled and followed Charlotte upstairs, one hand on the shining mahogany banister. To herself, she decided that he was all of a piece with his unusual daughter. What strange people these Brontës were! She was remembering her first sight of Charlotte at Miss Wooler's school at Roehead, in a far-off part of Yorkshire: of seeing the miserable, lonely little figure weeping quietly in the bay window of the schoolroom. She had gone up to her then to comfort her, and they had been friends from that moment. Poor Charlotte, who had seldom been away from home before; whose clothes were old-fashioned and quite unlike anybody else's. So shortsighted too, she held books up to her nose.

Yes, right from the first Ellen had made herself Charlotte's protectress. Yet presently, in some odd way, it became Charlotte who took the lead. Nobody ever laughed at Charlotte after they had known her a little.

Charlotte showed her visitor into the bedroom they were to share and then went downstairs again. Branwell had already carried up Ellen's trunk before them. Now he was waiting at the bottom of the staircase to see the vision from the outside world when she was ready to descend.

Moving aside to let Charlotte pass, he said in a low voice, "I thought her brother Henry might have come, too."

"Henry Nussey?" She looked surprised.

"Well, didn't you?"

She made no answer, and looked annoyed. Ellen's brother Henry was exceedingly handsome and just been ordained as a clergyman. Branwell had met him when he went to "The Rydings" to fetch Charlotte home again after her visit there.

"You interested him," Branwell was saying, unquenched by her annoyance. "I could see that. I don't think he'd ever met anyone like you before."

Charlotte ignored that remark, too. Branwell laughed his lazy, charming laugh. He was the only high-spirited member of the family, and he was fond of teasing. Like his sisters Anne and Charlotte he was below average height; and not particularly good-looking, but at sixteen years old he had an attractive manner and a witty tongue, and was such good company that nobody minded about his looks.

Charlotte went into the kitchen to make tea. Tabby, the servant, had already stirred up the fire, and the iron kettle swinging down from a hook and chain was puffing away. Aunt Branwell had brought down her special little silver teapot and the mahogany tea box, and placed them on the table near the door as she always did.

"Eh, but Miss Nussey's a bonny young la-ady!" Tabby obligingly swung the heavy kettle over the teapot.

"You've seen her, Tabby?"

"A' keeked out o' window when she ca-ame."

Charlotte dribbled the precious tea leaves in, and then waited while Tabby tilted the kettle over the pot. Tea was a very expensive luxury. Only Miss Branwell indulged as a rule, but this was a special occasion. Charlotte picked up the tray and carrying it upstairs again, knocked on the door of her aunt's room.

"Bring in the tea, my dear!"

Aunt Branwell was sitting in state, wearing her best

dress. Like her niece she was tiny. She wore a very large cap over auburn curls which bunched out from beneath it into a fringe. The girls had never discussed, even among themselves, whether the auburn color was natural or not.

Anne, the gentle, the pretty one of the family, sat at her aunt's feet. Beside them was the tea tray with its plate of delicately cut bread and butter which was to help sustain the visitor until suppertime.

Charlotte withdrew and went to her own room where she found Ellen had already unpacked. Then, hesitating, she lowered her voice and said, "Don't mind my aunt if she tells you we live in a fierce, uncomfortable place! The Branwells are Cornish you know. When my mother died, Aunt gave up everything—all her friends—to come north from Penzance and look after us. If she grumbles a little, it's natural."

Miss Branwell rose to her feet and greeted Ellen majestically. This room was her territory. Here she had transplanted her family treasures from the old home at Penzance. Her boat-shaped mahogany bedstead was half concealed behind a screen plastered with prints of Cornish scenery. Faded water colors showing the rocks and sea of her youth, hung on the walls. Here Miss Branwell was at home.

A small fire burned in the grate as it always did, winter and summer. "Come close and be warm," she begged, adding, "This terrible Yorkshire air bites hard."

Ellen smiled a little, but sat where she was told to sit. She was a Yorkshire girl herself and the room with its closed window felt stuffy and airless. She sipped her tea from the handleless cup, more like a small painted bowl, which Anne had given her. She bit daintily into a transparent slice of bread and butter, and hoped more solid food would be provided soon, for she was hungry after her journey.

"In my Cornish home," said Miss Branwell, "we were quite accustomed to semitropical vegetation; palms, for instance. When our soft winds blew along the coast, you could hear the rustle of palms for miles."

Charlotte gave her mischievous, crooked smile. "The winds didn't always blow soft, Aunt, did they?" she remarked.

"Of course storms occurred from time to time," her aunt conceded. . . . "May I give you a little more tea, Miss Nussey?"

When tea was finished, Anne, who had sat so quiet, leaving the conversation to the others, gathered the dishes together and stole out of the room with the tray. Charlotte and Ellen said good-by formally, as if they had been visiting in another house. When they stood in the passage again, Charlotte asked what Ellen would like to do between now and suppertime.

"Can't we go out on the moor? I haven't seen you for so long, Charlotte, there are a thousand things, private things, I want to talk about. And the moor would be a splendid place to discuss them!"

Ellen had remembered how, at Miss Wooler's School, Charlotte always struggled like a bird to be out of doors. How much more freely she had spoken of her thoughts and difficulties to her friend as soon as they were free of the house and under the empty sky.

She was surprised, therefore, when Charlotte seemed to hesitate, saying, "Are you sure you aren't too tired after your journey? Perhaps tomorrow . . ."

"Oh, tomorrow! Tomorrow it may be raining."

Charlotte nodded agreement. It was true. So Ellen went back to her room for her cloak. It would be fresh if not windy, upon Haworth Moor. As for Charlotte's hesitation about taking her there, of course that was all imagination.

When she came out on the landing again, she stopped dead. Surely the high newel post of the staircase had been perfectly plain and not carved with the figure of a hawk? Then the hawk's head twisted around suddenly, its bright, fierce eyes meeting hers. Ellen gave a little gasp. It was alive! Its beak looked cruel and sharp. It was motionless again, as if waiting for something or someone. She trembled, feeling that she could not possibly risk trying to pass it by going downstairs.

"What is it, Ellen?" Charlotte, standing invisible at the foot of the stairs, had heard the little half-gasp, half-shriek.

"The bird—the hawk!"

"It's all right, it's only Hero, Emily's tame hawk. He generally lives in a cage in her room, but sometimes he gets out."

"Oh, Charlotte, I'm such a little fool, but I'm afraid to pass him!"

Charlotte ran upstairs again and took Ellen's hand in hers. "Come, dear. Hero's only waiting for Emily to come back. He pays no attention to anyone else. She saved his life when he was young and half-frozen. She found him on our top step one morning after a snowstorm. She warmed him in the oven, and he follows, and waits for her."

"Wh-where *is* Emily?" Ellen said rather quaveringly, looking back at the immobile figure at the top of the stairs.

"Somewhere out on the moor."

It crossed Ellen's mind that Emily's presence on the moor seemed to have something to do with Charlotte's hesitation about going there. But that was absurd! Why should Emily take possession of the moor, and why should Charlotte, the elder sister, show any dread of meeting her there?

In any case, it wasn't very polite of Emily to run off out of doors instead of waiting to greet the visitor.

CHAPTER *Two*

The parsonage garden was very different from the one at Ellen's home, "The Rydings." There, smooth lawns dropped down in terraces crescented and banded with flower beds and finally stopped by a belt of trees. A belt of trees meant considerable land (because you can't have trees growing too near a house) and that, in turn, meant wealth and stately living.

Branwell Brontë was the only one of his family to be drawn toward wealth and stately living. He had winced at the thought of Ellen Nussey seeing their own shabby garden. There was scarcely a thing in it except some straggling bushes, and a graveyard bounded it instead of trees. A gate led out into the steep lane up which Ellen had traveled an hour or two ago, and which curved on past the house toward the moors. Charlotte had already turned to the left when Ellen, who had stopped to glance back in the direction of the village, pulled at her arm to stop her.

"Look! There's a poor man lying on the road! He must have had an accident."

Charlotte paused, looked back, then wrinkled her nose in disgust. "It's only John Fothergill and he's drunk. He's always getting thrown out of 'The Black Bull' and lying down on the road to sleep it off."

She led the way very decidedly and Ellen had to follow. The lane had shrunk to a cart track now. It was bordered by dry-stone dykes low enough for them to see the whole of the moor spread out before them. The gray stone walls threaded it like veins, hemming in a few scattered farms and isolated stone buildings.

Through the hush of late afternoon, Ellen could hear the sound of water running. It was the little gray river, slatelike and scarcely moving, which would grow to a torrent in winter. Charlotte was standing still. She was listening to it with delight.

"Can you wonder that we always choose to come out here?" she asked. "You've seen a sample of our village life already. The people are brutal—like animals some of them. They live to drink and fight. We never go through the village unless we can help it, Anne and Emily and I."

"You are the rector's daughter, and you speak of his parish like that?" Ellen felt a little shocked.

Charlotte said quickly, "Oh, we do our duty, of course. We teach in Sunday school, and if anyone is ill we visit them. But we're forced to keep to ourselves, for there is no one with whom we have anything in common here—no one at all."

"But what do you *do* all day? Besides parish work, I mean."

Charlotte took a step nearer her friend. Her large, shortsighted eyes peered into Ellen's face as she said, "You won't tell anyone? You won't laugh? . . . Well, we write stories."

"Why, Charlotte, how clever! What kind of stories?"

"Very romantic and exciting and—and fantastical."

Ellen remembered something. "Of course you invented wonderful stories at Miss Wooler's. You called it 'making out' something or other. Like that night when the wind howled like a voice down the passage and we begged you to 'make out' what it was saying, and you told such a horrific story, poor little Bessie Smith took screaming hysterics."

Charlotte's own face had grown suddenly pale. She put out her hand to stop Ellen. "It was wrong of me. . . . I made a vow that night, never to frighten either myself or anyone else like that again. Imagination is too powerful a weapon to use lightly. It should stay in its sheath."

"But what do you write about, then?"

"Well—it began one night when we were all sitting by the firelight and Tabby *would not* give us a candle. She's very sparing with candles, you know. She makes us sit without them till it's perfectly dark. So, to pass the time we each chose an Island and placed our favorite heroes there. From that we invented two countries, Angria and Gondal. We gave them characters and laws and churches and schools. We have written about them for years."

Ellen was only half-listening now. The full sweep of Haworth Moor lay before them. In spite of the evening stillness, the landscape seemed to shimmer with a curious movement of its own. She knew it was only the air passing over the heath and the grasses and ruffling the satin-gray surface of the water in the stream. But it gave an unreal tinge to everything, like a landscape seen in sleep.

About half a mile away an enormous gray rock stretched like a hand over part of the moor. The little stream they were following made toward it. There was even a trodden path going in that direction; very lightly trodden it was true, as if nothing heavier than the feet of the girls from the parsonage ever went that way.

Ellen's boots were town-made of fine leather. The track they stood on was stony. The little path looked soft and inviting. She said, "Let's go this way, Charlotte," and stepped on it.

It was only wide enough for one. But instead of immediately following, Charlotte seemed to be standing still on the verge. Again that odd hesitation. Ellen stopped and turned round.

"What is the matter? Are you tired? Would you prefer that we went back?"

"N-no, not if you feel inclined this way. I only thought the path might be damp."

The moss did squelch slightly beneath one's feet. But it was such a brilliant, such a wicked green that it lured one on. Like most Yorkshire people, Ellen called the little stream a beck. And the beck flowed on by its green carpet until at last the shadow of the rock fell across it, seeming to smite it and send it tumbling down into a deep pool half hidden by ferns.

As the two girls approached, the ferns parted violently and a third girl sprang up, staring accusingly at Charlotte across the water. She was much taller than either Charlotte or Anne. Handsomer too, though Anne's beautiful gentle eyes gave her another charm.

"Charlotte!" The voice was reproachful, angry even.

"It is nearly suppertime, Emily. And I wanted you to meet Ellen. She arrived hours ago."

Emily gave Ellen a quick, proud look, like the look the

hawk had given her there on the staircase. There was the same haughty turn of head; the same disdain of the stranger. Ellen knew now why Charlotte had hesitated about taking her on to the moor, especially by this path. It had led straight to Emily's private retreat.

They went back along it toward the cart track and the parsonage again, walking in single file. Emily led the way with such swift, long steps it was almost impossible to keep up with her. Quite impossible to have any conversation, which was perhaps her idea. Ellen walked next, wishing she could slip her arm into Charlotte's and feel protected against this wild, fierce sister of hers. But Emily was polite enough to wait for the other two once she had reached the cart track where they could once more walk abreast.

She didn't look at them, however, as they approached. Ellen noticed that her eyes seldom met anyone else's unless she was startled and annoyed as when interrupted down by the pool. They slid to right or left of the person in front of her, or sought the open sky and the hills with relief. Now they looked beyond and far away as if something had caught her attention. The other two turned round to see what had made Emily's lips part and her eyes dilate.

At first Ellen saw nothing extraordinary, beyond the wild landscape and the clouds that had begun to roll down upon it. Then she saw the light shaft between the clouds. It was playing over the heights. As they watched, it parted the clouds again like a sword and a gray ridge appeared on the horizon.

"That's Top Withens," Charlotte informed her friend.

"What a weird, lonely place to live!"

"Why do you think so?" It was almost the first time

Emily had spoken. It was a deep, husky voice and it held a note of scorn. "Is it not a fine thing to live away from the world on the top of a hill?"

"But—how do people get their food, their necessities, so high up and far from a road? For I don't see any."

Charlotte laughed. Even Emily smiled. Charlotte said, "Ellen dear, there's nobody there! Not even a house, or at any rate, not a whole one. There's 'Top Withens,' of course, but that's a ruin."

Ellen stared, fascinated. "One could imagine a robber's castle perched there, or maybe some great lonely mansion."

Emily gave her a sudden piercing look. "You can see that, too?"

"Top Withens," Ellen repeated slowly. "What a good name. It's on top of the world, on the very heights. And the wind will wuther about it. . . ."

"There! I've a better one still. Wuthering Heights. Don't you hear the wind in the very name?"

Emily had scarcely finished the sentence when the wind, which must ever be blowing up there though the valley was still enough, swept the curtain of mist finally together, and the high ridge was blotted out in a second.

Emily seemed to have warmed a little to Ellen now. She had recovered, too, from her annoyance at being tracked to her secret hiding place. She began to talk quite amicably as they retraced their steps along the cart track. Presently they came into sight of civilization—though a rough, wild civilization—with the curve of the village street and the gate of the parsonage and the motionless, tumbled figure of John Fothergill still lying in the middle of the road.

Ellen looked away from him; Charlotte ignored him and ran to open the garden gate for her guest. But Emily stopped a moment to say, "I'll give an arm to John; he's doing himself no good lying there."

For the life of her, Ellen couldn't have offered to help. Everything disagreeable had always been shrouded from view at "The Rydings." Impossible to imagine tiny, fragile Charlotte being able to help either. It was obvious that she wasn't going to try, but she gave a glance of admiration toward her sister all the same. Emily was certainly much taller and stronger. She was shaking John Fothergill, urging him to stand up. Her tones were commanding enough for him to look up at her first, in a dazed way, and then to scramble to his feet with her help.

Ellen saw the two figures, one supporting the other, disappear round the steep bend. She thought of the battered young hawk, saved and tamed by Emily, too. She went slowly after Charlotte thinking: Emily omits politeness, but she is without fear and has great pity. I must remember that.

There were only the two sitting rooms in the parsonage, and Mr. Brontë's was inviolate. Nobody entered it unless by express invitation. He usually had breakfast and supper in there alone. The room to the left of the front door was the general parlor where supper was to be served that evening. Ellen could see a cheerful fire blazing and the mahogany table already set, as she passed its doorway on her way upstairs to take off her bonnet.

As Charlotte followed her into the bedroom she asked,

"Is it a secret about the stories you write? I thought it best to ask in case the others——"

"Why, yes, I suppose it's a secret. At least, the others who don't know you as I do, might want it kept so."

Ellen said wistfully, "I wish you'd show me something you've written."

"Oh, I can *show* you!"

There was a small rosewood writing desk deposited neatly on the floor under the open window. Charlotte felt in her pocket for the key. Then she went down on her knees (for the desk was only a shallow, polished box with a lid), opened it, and brought out a handful of tiny books. These she handed up to her friend.

Ellen looked at them with wonder. They were only about a couple of inches square, and homemade from little bits of faded paper sewn together. She could just make out the titles of some of them, printed neatly in ink on the covers:

An Extraordinary Dream. By Lord C. Wellesley.
Lines to the River Aragua. By the Marquis of Douro.
The Green Dwarf. By the Lord Charles Albert Florian Wellesley.
Strange Events. By Lord C. A. F. Wellesley.

Charlotte almost snatched them out of Ellen's hands again. She knelt down to lock them up once more, saying in a muffled voice, "I wrote them years ago. I can write better than such nonsense now."

"For author, you have taken the name . . ."

"The various names belonging to the Duke of Wellington. You know how I always admired him. And writers—

women writers particularly—should be modest enough not to use their own names. What has their professional life to do with their private one?"

"Charlotte, please. Could you not let me see something you are writing now?"

A faint flush came into Charlotte's cheeks. "I can't. Everything we write is private, among ourselves."

Ellen was not a businessman's daughter for nothing. "But don't you want to sell what you write someday? To be famous and known?"

The flush deepened on Charlotte's cheeks. "That isn't what we write for! I can't explain it, you wouldn't understand. It is to create one's own world—another world from this. It gives one such a feeling of power!"

"And you can do it! I know you can. The stories you made up at Miss Wooler's made cold shivers run up our backs!"

Charlotte shrugged her neat, small shoulders. "It was easy enough. But to choose the right words on paper is another thing. I dare say the scribbles with which we amuse ourselves are at least teaching us to do that."

The iron clang of a bell at the foot of the stairs reminded them it was suppertime. Ellen looked startled for a moment and, noticing this, her friend said quickly, "Another thing I must warn you about. I had nearly forgot. If you hear shots being fired out of the back door in the morning, pay no attention. It will only be Papa."

"Shots?" Ellen asked faintly.

"He loads two pistols every night and takes them up to his bedroom. I don't want to alarm you, but this is a very rough neighborhood. We have never been broken into, and everyone treats us with respect. But only a few years ago . . . Anyway, Papa always goes armed to bed. And then you know, he doesn't think it safe to keep loaded pistols about the house during the day. So he empties them through the back door as soon as he's up and dressed. That's what the noise will be."

"Thank you for telling me."

Ellen followed her little hostess downstairs to supper. Remembering the queer, strange stories Charlotte used to make up at school, she couldn't help thinking that life at Haworth Parsonage was almost as queer and strange.

CHAPTER *Three*

Each morning, early, Mr. Brontë rose, dressed, went downstairs and opening the back door, fired two loud shots out of it. Having thus wakened his family effectively, he retired to his study and read till breakfast time.

Meanwhile Tabby prepared the breakfast. She made porridge and carried the steaming bowls into the parlor, flanking them with a large jug of milk. Ellen, used to beginning the day more daintily with toast and a lightly boiled egg, did her best to enjoy the hot oatmeal. After breakfast, there were the household chores. Ellen insisted on taking her turn at them, and quite won Tabby's heart by the way she peeled potatoes for their dinner.

Anne went upstairs to read with Miss Branwell. Emily vanished on to the moor, and her brother (having been told bluntly that his presence was not required) would saunter off to the village. So the two friends were left together, to sit in the garden if it was fine or in the parlor if it rained.

Ellen had brought some embroidery with her. It was handy to bend her head over when she asked Charlotte a direct question or two.

"Now you are grown-up, Charlotte, what are you going to *do?*"

"Do? Why stay at home and teach the other two, of course. Papa coaches Branwell, and I teach Emily and Anne."

Ellen bit off a thread. "Emily's old enough surely to teach Anne herself. Then you'd be free."

"I don't know what you mean by that," Charlotte said rather stiffly. "I'm free enough already."

"But what about getting married and having a home of your own?"

Unexpectedly, Charlotte laughed. "Who would marry anyone as plain-looking as me?"

Ellen said carefully, "You know I don't think you plain. And Henry thinks you've got lovely eyes. He said so."

"I'm greatly obliged for his kind opinion." The stiffness had come back to her manner. Ellen, warned by it, dropped Henry hastily.

"Well, perhaps the girls need you just now. But you really must go out into the world sometime. How else could you meet anyone except tiresome curates?"

"But I *shall* go out into the world. I must. I must earn my living somehow, you know."

"Don't be offended, dearest; but if you found a good man—a clergyman, say, who would give you a comfortable home and support you——"

Charlotte interrupted her so quickly and angrily that Ellen raised her eyes from her embroidery, astonished. Her friend's small figure was actually trembling. The great hazel eyes flashed fire.

"Sell myself to the first bidder who offered to keep me?

Oh, I know it's done every day! Every girl nowadays is taught to attract a rich husband, no matter what misery follows! I'd rather earn my own living a thousand times, than do that!"

"But how? You know how you dread meeting strangers. You hate leaving home, why, it took weeks of letter writing to persuade you even to visit me!"

Charlotte's head drooped a little. The fire died down. "I know. And I'm not really very fond of children either, but I must teach them. It's all I've been trained to do."

"You mean—be a governess?"

Charlotte nodded. "Of course."

Ellen could say nothing more. For people like the Brontës, governessing was the only sort of paid work they could find. Yet Charlotte was independent and hated taking orders. She wasn't very fond of children. And worst of all (as Ellen knew well), she was so shy the thought of meeting strangers had always terrified her and almost made her ill. Ellen felt very sorry for Charlotte.

The girls took advantage of the fine weather to go for picnics and long walks over the moors. Anne and Emily quietly shared some of Charlotte's housework so as to leave her free to enjoy the company of her friend. When Charlotte protested, they pointed out that it was her duty to entertain Ellen. So she promised herself that she would shoulder some of *their* tasks after Ellen had gone back home. It was such an unaccustomed joy to have a real friend of her own age to walk and talk with!

Presently, however, Ellen's visit to Haworth drew to a close. Everyone regretted that she was going away. Miss Branwell liked her; Tabby adored her, and young Branwell followed her every movement with admiration, a fact of which she was well aware. Even Emily the silent approved of her. The night before she left the parsonage, Anne and Charlotte were quite downcast.

And yet . . .

Ellen knew quite well that she had been only a small, sparkling pebble thrown into the deep waters of the Brontë home. Once out of sight, she would soon be forgotten (except of course, by Charlotte) and the quiet parsonage would settle to stillness again.

Morning broke, clear and bright. For the last time Ellen opened her eyes to that staring, uncurtained window. For the last time, putting her toes out of bed, she scuffled about for her soft bedroom slippers to protect her feet from the cold of the uncarpeted floor. The carriage would arrive for her sometime about noon. The horses must rest and John, the coachman, eat his dinner while they ate theirs. And then the long drive home.

Branwell had posted himself as usual, at the end of the village street. He came running into the house with the news. "It's coming! There's somebody in it already, though. It looks like your brother Henry."

Henry Nussey was a tall, handsome young man as fair as his sister, but slightly pompous and rather self-satisfied. He explained that he had come to escort his sister home, but Branwell the quick-witted noticed how his rather protuberant blue eyes sought Charlotte's constantly. Charlotte would not look at him, however. All through dinner she kept her eyes on her plate.

They had decided to give the horses another hour before subjecting them to the long pull home across the moors. "Will you show me the garden?" Henry asked Charlotte, excluding everyone else so pointedly that she was forced to step out of doors with him while the others remained in the parlor.

"We haven't a proper garden really. The wind kills most things, but those currant bushes at the bottom. Do you—do you like currants, Mr. Nussey?"

Henry smiled condescendingly at her evident confusion. She knew what was coming, did she?

"If *you* like them I shall plant them at once when I take over the parsonage of my new living. I suppose Ellen told you I've just been appointed to a very good living?"

Charlotte fixed her eyes on the tombstones over the wall beyond the currant bushes. "I congratulate you," she said in a low voice.

"Yes. Not every young man of my age, practically straight from college, is given such a plum to begin with. But I dare say the Bishop realized . . . Anyhow, the parsonage is excellent, too; rather better (if I may say so) than yours. It has more commodious stabling. But then the last incumbent was the younger son of an earl."

"Were his horses superior, too?"

He glanced sharply at Charlotte, but was satisfied to see her usual modest, downcast look. Just for the moment he had thought she was laughing at him. Of course, the thought was ridiculous.

"In fact it wants only one thing."

"Really?" The large, golden-brown eyes suddenly shone full on him, disconcerting him for the moment. "What can that be?"

"A woman to run it. Somebody brought up in modest circumstances (so that there should be no waste), yet accustomed to the duties of a clergyman's household. Someone——"

"Oh, I understand you now! I'll ask Tabby if she can recommend anyone from the village. You would require her to be a good plain cook, I suppose?"

Devil take the little creature! She really *is* laughing. Oh, well, thought Henry, relaxing his own solemnity slightly, one likes to be teased sometimes, so long as it doesn't go too far. Besides, one likes her all the better for not appearing to grasp her chance too eagerly.

"Thank you, but I was scarcely talking about household staff. What I need is a mistress to command them and —er—me." (But he doesn't mean that last bit, Charlotte told herself, trying hard to stifle her inward laughter.)

"Oh, I see. You want to get married?"

"I have been trying to indicate it."

Henry couldn't help glancing at the clock on the church tower as he spoke. He would have pulled out his watch, but it didn't seem quite right to interrupt a proposal in such a way. Still, they had a long drive before them, and somehow Charlotte had prevented him from coming to the point sooner.

"If you will have me, Charlotte. I flatter myself I can make you happy and comfortable. In return, you know the duties of a clergyman's wife. Ellen speaks highly of your character in every way. You are a little shy perhaps, but that will soon wear off."

Charlotte turned and began, very deliberately, to walk back to the house. "Thank you for your kind offer, Mr. Nussey, but I'm afraid I must decline."

"You—you decline my proposal?"

He could scarcely believe his ears.

"Yes. We aren't really suited, you know."

Still, he couldn't believe it. He glanced up at the

shabby, bleak parsonage, the uncurtained windows, the wild and neglected garden. And this little creature, had no looks to commend her (fine eyes, though) no prospects, no dowry even. That she should actually be unwilling to exchange her poverty-stricken condition for the one he was offering her was insulting!

She had reached the house and disappeared through the open doorway. He followed her, frustrated and angry. Behind his back he could hear the carriage horses being led down the lane. Why, there wasn't even a carriage sweep in front of the house. Ellen would have to have her luggage actually lifted out into the road.

Ellen was coming down the staircase dressed and ready for her journey. Mr. Brontë had stepped out of his study to bid her good-by. Anne, the gentle and loving, hung round her neck. Charlotte had turned and was escorting her friend out of the house again.

Henry bowed and managed to say good-by to them all. He was just going after the two girls when there was a sudden whirr of wings and the tightening of talons through his new broadcloth jacket. Emily's hawk had alighted, startlingly, on his shoulder.

"Devil take that bird!" he cried out.

It was the last straw.

Emily, standing in the shadow of the staircase, gave a low whistle. The bird lifted itself on its outstretched wings and exchanged his shoulder for hers. Discomfited, he blundered out after the others. And Charlotte, who had heard him exclaim, actually looked back at him with a wicked smile.

"Oh fie, Mr. Nussey!" she called after him. "Recollect, you're a clergyman now!"

He was thankful when the coachman whipped up the horses and they began to plunge down the steep village street. Ellen blew kisses as long as the little figure standing at the parsonage gate was in sight. Then she leaned back, giving glances toward her brother's handsome profile, but not daring to ask the question she burned to ask, until she could contain it no longer.

"Did—did you propose?" she murmured a little tremblingly.

"She refused me."

"What!"

"She seems to have other plans," Henry said coldly.

"But—she must earn her own living then! Poor Charlotte, there's nothing left for her to do but to be a governess!"

"Let her be a governess." Henry said more coldly still. Then his coldness left him suddenly. A sudden flush of anger took its place, blowing away all his fine manners for the moment, and bringing him back to the solid, Yorkshire dialect of his youth.

"The girl's daft!"

Now, behind them, the shadows began to lengthen across the village street of Haworth. The air was very still. The long grasses scarcely stirred against the stones in the graveyard. Charlotte, cleaning her bedroom, shook a duster over the sill and paused to breathe in the evening fragrance. Much as she would miss Ellen, it was nice to step back into one's own private world. That private world of the imagination which had been banished while they had a visitor and which now possessed her once more. The rest of the house was silent. She had this hour to herself.

She stooped and lifted the little rosewood desk off the

floor. Paper to write on was always an urgent consideration in the parsonage. One had to walk to Keighley to buy notebooks, four miles there and four miles back; and notebooks were expensive anyway.

All three girls had taught themselves to write in such tiny script that even a scrap of paper went a long way. Charlotte was sure she had saved two empty flyleaves from one of their books. Yes, there they were. The edge of the dressing table was near enough to the window to serve as a desk and give her the benefit of what light still remained in the sky.

The plot of a wild, romantic story had laid in her mind already, pushed aside until the pleasure of Ellen's visit should be over. She wrote "The Dark Lover by Lord A. Wellington" at the top of the first page, and then began. He was swarthy, and short, with powerful shoulders and an ugly, intelligent face. He could be charming when he wished, but sometimes interestingly moody and silent.

He was as unlike Henry Nussey as he could possibly be.

CHAPTER *Four*

Summer and winter. Summer and winter. In winter the wind from the moors blew snow against the closed windows of the parsonage. In summer, when the windows were thrown open, a honey scent was blown in from the moors, the currant bushes became frilled with green, and the girls and their brother could once more spend their days out of doors in the wild freedom of the hills.

Unfortunately Emily lost her hawk. But she came on a goose with a broken leg, brought it home and nursed it. It must have got lost in unaccustomed flight from one of the small hill farms, but as nobody claimed it, she kept it and presently, because it seemed lonely, she bought another out of her own pocket money to keep it company. She called the first Adelaide, after the Queen Consort of William IV; and the second, Victoria, after the young Princess Victoria.

Aunt Branwell quite approved. "Fattened up, one will do very nicely for Michaelmas dinner, and the other for Christmas Day." Emily shuddered but held her peace.

Winter came early this particular year. The cold wind whistled under the kitchen door until Tabby made a draught-excluder out of rags formed into a long sausage and laid it along the bottom of the door. The geese, who slept in an open shed, would come to the back door, shivering. They knew if they looked pathetic enough Tabby would let them into the kitchen to stand on one leg before the fire.

Then the snow came.

"Eh, the poor beasts!" Tabby looked pityingly at the birds while Charlotte was taking a dish out of the oven for supper. "I'd gladly like to let them be here all t'night, seeing 'shed's open and freezing cold. But they'd make a right muck o' my kitchen floor."

"Honk!" said Victoria, fixing Charlotte with a bright, hopeful eye.

Charlotte considered. "What about the turf room? They could roost on top of the pile of turfs. The floor's such a mess in there anyway, it wouldn't make much difference."

There was a little room to the left of the front door, right behind the parlor. It was empty and used to store the piles of turf, cut from the moors in autumn and used for the fires.

"Eh, that'll be fine! I'll drive the birds in at bedtime and out again into ya-ard first thing i' th' mornings."

So the big birds were solemnly escorted, lurching, across the passage each night and into the turf room. Whether Aunt Branwell knew or not about this proceeding, Charlotte did not inquire. Anne, Emily, and Branwell did, of course; the last in particular thinking it a great joke. Tabby took care to hustle the geese back through the kitchen and out at the yard door each morning early.

Presently the muffled honks from the turf room must

have made Aunt Branwell aware of what was going on. By then, she chose to ignore it. It was Mr. Brontë himself who, coming out of his study at an unusually early hour of the evening for him, nearly fell over a large white shape.

Charlotte was escorting them this evening, as Tabby had already gone up to bed. Her heart had gone into her mouth a little, when she heard the click of the study door opening just as the two geese crossed the passage. The light from the oil lamp high in its bracket seemed to make them visible enough. Yet Mr. Brontë walked straight into them and only saved himself from a fall by clutching hold of the wall.

"Oh, I'm sorry, Papa! We've been letting them roost in the turf room during the cold weather."

"I did not notice them." Mr. Brontë spoke mildly. "I merely thought the shadows looked a little strange——"

"Perhaps you require new spectacles?" she asked as she shooed the birds into the turf room for the night. But her father did not think it time to incur that expense, and proceeded on his way upstairs.

It was cosy in the parsonage in winter, despite the wind and the snow outside. Tabby kept roaring fires, so that her "bairns," as she called them, should not catch cold. She baked potatoes in their jackets and brought a steaming bowl of them to the table. Miss Branwell liked hers delicately mashed, with butter and salt and pepper, and Tabby sniffed at this particularity. Tea, too, at ten shillings a pound, made in her silver teapot and carried upstairs along with thin paperlike bread and butter seemed just affectation and nonsense to the old Yorkshire woman, though she herself was never required to make it or carry it up.

The girls had plenty of work to do during the day.

There was bedmaking, peeling potatoes to help Tabby, and Emily took on the duty of scrubbing the sandstone floors. But each night after supper, when the fire blazed cheerfully and Mr. Brontë was safely gone to his study, the three of them sat round the dining table with pens and scraps of paper on which to write down more adventures of the inhabitants of the imaginary country of Angria.

There was silence except for the squeaking of pens, while imaginations raced far beyond the stone walls of the parsonage. Dimly Charlotte would be aware of the door opening and their father putting his head in to say, "Good night, my loves. Don't stay up too late," and then of his heavy tread pausing, halfway upstairs, to wind the grandfather clock that stood there in a niche.

Miss Branwell, too, would have gone to bed. Branwell would be down in the village with some of his friends. So there was nothing to disturb them except the gradual dying down of the fire, until the thought of tomorrow's tasks at last drew them again out of Angria and upstairs to their pillows.

Now it was 1835, two years since Ellen Nussey's visit. Charlotte, the eldest, was nineteen, and Anne the youngest, fifteen. Emily was to go to Charlotte's old school as a senior pupil. Even Anne's education would soon be finished. Charlotte had to face the fact that very soon, her reason for staying at home would be gone. She would have to go into the world—the real world she hated and feared—and earn her living by teaching strangers instead.

Unless . . . but the little stitched-together books held nothing, surely, that would interest a publisher and bring in some money? The tales were too short, for one thing. They would never make a full-sized book. Perhaps they might be considered as exercises, helping her to get her ideas down on paper, so that someday she might even see a real book of hers in print. She never dared to tell such imaginings to any of the others. They seemed quite happy writing down plots and adventures for the imaginary country they had invented, though Charlotte had an idea that Emily was working on something else. A novel? Or poems? If she didn't dare to tell her own imaginings, she dared not ask about Emily's.

Winter mildened into spring, and the light strengthened so that Branwell could at last begin the large, important portrait of his three sisters together which he had planned to do. They were all fond of drawing, but Branwell was best at it. He had had lessons in oils. If this portrait was good enough to impress his father, then perhaps he might be allowed to go to London and study painting seriously and be a real artist, which was what he wanted above all things.

"Not so serious, Emily! . . . Anne, are you *sure* you've done your hair exactly the same as yesterday?" The artist fussed about his easel, trying to place them in the same positions they had taken up during the first sittings. Painting one sitter was bad enough; painting three was the devil. And yet the three girls began to spring out vividly on the canvas. Branwell's picture was crude and inexpert, but he did have the gift of bringing his sitters to life.

Mr. Brontë was very pleased with the painting. He had always been proud of his son's gifts. His daughters, being young ladies, were not supposed to have any ambitions, but he agreed at once to let Branwell seek his fortune in London.

On a warm July day in that summer of 1835 Charlotte stole up to her room, unlocked her little rosewood desk and began to write a letter to Ellen.

"We are all about to divide, break up, separate." She wrote. "Emily is going to school, Branwell is going to London, and I am going to be a governess. . . . Emily and I leave home on the 29th of this month; the idea of being together consoles us both somewhat, and, truth, since I must enter a situation, 'my lines have fallen on pleasant places.' I both love and respect Miss Wooler."

Yes, she was going back to Miss Wooler's School at Roehead, where she and Ellen had first met. She was going back, not as a pupil, but to teach. Emily was coming partly to help and partly to learn. Anne would follow later. That was the plan.

Charlotte's pen dropped from her fingers. She was seeing Miss Wooler again in her mind's eye; remembering her own arrival at Roehead years ago, a terrified schoolgirl. The handsome house once more loomed before her, its bow windows glittering in the sun. Meadows and parks stretched in front of it. The landscape was charming, not bleak as at Haworth. But what did that matter to little, homesick Charlotte as she was then?

Only Miss Wooler comforted her; made her feel at home. She could see her now, almost as if she had entered the room. A short, stout person, but with great dignity, and dressed always in white. Was it Ellen who first said she looked like a Lady Abbess? More important, she was kind. She was understanding. She had drawn Charlotte out and had taught her many things. Charlotte was to look on Miss Wooler, all her life, as a friend.

She signed the letter to Ellen, folded and addressed it. Her box stood packed already. Branwell would cord it for her. A few days later, she and Emily left home.

A great silence fell on the parsonage. Branwell was usually down in the village. Anne crept gently about, trying not to disturb her father or Aunt Branwell, both of whom spent most of the day shut up in their own rooms. Trying not to feel lonely, or frightened at the prospect of following her sisters, later, to Roehead.

And then, suddenly one day, Emily came home.

Nobody was in the least surprised to see her walk in. Emily could not be penned up in a boarding school any more than Hero, her hawk could be penned in the parsonage. She told them little, beyond such things as, that they had expected her to play ball games like a child. It was Charlotte who wrote down what Emily felt.

"Liberty was the breath of Emily's nostrils; without it she perished. The change from her own home to a school, and from her own very noiseless, very secluded but unrestricted and unartificial mode of life to one of disciplined routine was what she failed in enduring. Every morning when she woke, the visions of home and the moors rushed on her and darkened and saddened the day that lay before her. Nobody knew what ailed her but me. I felt in my heart she would die if she did not go home."

So Emily slipped into her accustomed duties again, doing all the hard work for Tabby who was now almost seventy.

Now it was nearly Christmas once more. Victoria and Adelaide began to look a little apprehensive. When they saw Miss Branwell surveying them from her window, they scuttled back into their shed *ga-ga-ing* loudly. They were remarkably silent too, in the turf room at night. So many of their relations had died sudden deaths round about Christmas time that no doubt they thought it wiser to be discreet.

Miss Branwell did remark on their plumpness once or twice; but Emily's large eyes were immediately filled with such alarm, and Anne looked so mutinous that finally, to set their minds at rest, she commented, "I suppose we shall have one of Tabby's good steak-and-kidney puddings this Christmas as usual," and let the matter alone.

Branwell had returned from an unsuccessful visit to London. During the Christmas holidays he and Charlotte walked the moors together while he poured out his hopes and ambitions in her ear.

"I feel I'm an artist. I know it! If I don't succeed in painting my way to fame I shall write my way there."

It was Charlotte's own secret dream, but she had always felt too humble to say it aloud. Now Branwell was saying it, and saying it with an assurance which startled and somehow frightened her.

"You have talent," she replied cautiously. "You have far more daring and vigorous attack than any of us. At any rate, if painting fails, you can try literature instead."

"I shall try *both*. But I don't need to try, I know I can succeed in one course or the other . . ." Then a shade came over his face. "The devil of it is, I must be sure of earning my living first. And you're in the same boat."

Her heart warmed at his perception. She gave his arm a little squeeze of gratitude. She hadn't needed to tell him how much she had dreaded going out into the world. If only she could make the necessary money by writing at home! *He* didn't mind the world, he liked it. She tried to shut her mind to the fact that Branwell only wanted fame so that the world would like and admire him in return.

But now he had forgotten her and was going back to himself again. "I thought of writing to Mr. Wordsworth to ask his opinion," he was saying grandly. "After all, study at the Royal Academy may not suit me."

"Write to Mr. Wordsworth!" She gasped at his daring.

"Why not? I've a few poems, trifles knocked off when I felt like it. I flatter myself they show what I can do. A line from a poet like Wordsworth, and I'm made."

"You don't think it would be—presumptuous?"

He stared at her in genuine amazement. "Among the younger men, who is there worth sixpence? I dare say he would be delighted to discover new talent. I shall write as soon as the Christmas fuss is over."

After he had gone Charlotte walked slowly upstairs to her room. She meant to write a letter to Ellen, but the idea of Branwell having the presumption to write to a great poet like Wordsworth and ask advice quite filled her mind instead.

Like all her family she adored poetry. There were even a few poems of her own, written up here in secret, not read aloud at the dining-room table as she sometimes read out her violent romances. On a corner of her dressing table stood a little pile of leather-covered volumes. The print was cruelly small. But Charlotte knew their contents by heart. She pulled out the one containing Wordsworth's poems and turned over its pages thoughtfully.

Here was "The Solitary Reaper," one of her favorites:

Behold her, single in the field,
Yon solitary Highland lass!
Reaping and singing by herself——

That was what she, Charlotte, did. But what to reap? And here was another that always made her heart lift with joy:

The Rainbow comes and goes,
And lovely is the Rose,
The Moon doth with delight
Look round her when the heavens are bare,
Waters on a starry night
Are beautiful and fair; . . .

She and Branwell had once walked over the moors by starlight and looked at the pricking lights reflected in the beck. They were, indeed, "beautiful and fair." Perhaps after all, Branwell was right in aiming high. Perhaps nobody but a first-rate poet *could* tell them if their own work was good or not.

She pushed the little book back into place, next to the *Selected Works of Robert Southey*. Her fingers hesitated, then pulled out the latter. A page opened where it had opened often before. As much as Charlotte worshiped the Duke of Wellington, she detested his enemy, Napoleon Bonaparte. And she loved exciting words, much rhetoric, violent feeling, like:

Woe, woe to England! woe and endless shame,
If this heroic land,
False to her feelings and unspotted fame,

Hold out the olive to the Tyrant's hand!
Woe to the world, if Buonaparte's throne
Be suffered still to stand!

That was the kind of writing which stirred her! Proud defiance and grand words. The sort of thing in fact, that she wrote herself.

Dared she show some of her work to Mr. Southey and ask his advice?

The sudden thought sent a stab through her mind like an electric shock. She stood rigid in the middle of the little room, staring down at her desk. What was there in it to show anyone, much less the Poet Laureate of England? A few poems, tucked in beside the dreamlike fairy-tale stories that she knew now were only practice pieces. But Mr. Southey was a poet, too. And why not, if one was to take advice from anyone, try the best?

Quickly, quickly, before her resolution could waver, she drew the verses out from between the tiny homemade books of stories by Lord Charles Wellesley and the rest. Quickly she sat down and began writing a letter to Mr. Southey. She had meant it to be short and to the point. But once she began, she found herself describing her hopes and longings, her restricted life and her need to earn money. Only when she had almost reached the end of her treasured sheet of good notepaper did she remember to beg his pardon for her intrusion, and to plead with him for an answer.

She would not tell even her sisters what she had done. She knew his address—so did most people in England, so famous was he. But she realized her ignorance of forms and proper designations once it came to writing his name on the outside of the neat little packet. Did one write "Robert Southey, Esq.," or simply "The Poet Laureate"?

She wrote both to be on the safe side, adding "Greta Hall, Keswick, Cumberland" on the packet. Then she slipped out of the house with it, eager to post it before her courage failed.

It almost did, as she approached the tiny shop with its counter for postal business. Mr. Feathers was one of her father's churchwardens. He might bring himself to inquire what business she had with the Poet Laureate? Possibly it would be better to wait until the next time she went to Keighley and post it there. But if she waited, she knew she would never post it at all.

Suddenly she spied the slipshod figure of Sarah Thwaites coming down the street toward her. Sarah had been in her Sunday-school class, and Charlotte had once or twice thought despairingly that even Saint Paul could have made nothing of her. Why, she was too stupid even to learn to read! She would never bother to glance at the address on the packet. If Mr. Feathers asked her any questions she could only gape.

"I want you to post this packet for me, Sarah," Charlotte told her abruptly. "Here is the money. If it isn't correct, I shall pay the difference another time."

Not even waiting to see if Sarah did what she was told, Charlotte turned back and ran up the hill again, toward the parsonage.

CHAPTER *Five*

Their simple Christmas dinner was held without any decorations or fuss. Indeed, decorations and Christmas trees were not yet the fashion in England. The year 1836 broke cold and wild over the parsonage roof. Charlotte still had a little holiday time left. Every morning she watched anxiously to see if Mr. Feathers would bring her a reply from the Poet Laureate. Branwell had kept his word and written to Wordsworth. He made no bones about calling at the post office daily, and every morning Mr. Feathers gave him the same answer.

"Nowt for 'e, Mr. Branwell. Is it a loov-letter ye be so anxious about?"

Fortunately the business of his departure for London took the edge off Mr. Wordsworth's extraordinary indifference to a young Yorkshireman's genius. Charlotte said nothing about her own disappointment at not hearing from Mr. Southey. She went quietly back to Miss Wooler's, taking Anne with her. It was not until March, when she had quite given up hope, that a letter came from the poet at last.

She could scarcely breathe as she opened it. Would

Mr. Southey allow her to hope that she could earn her living by her pen, so that she need never go out into the world again? He wrote lengthily and kindly. He explained that a mishap had prevented him from writing before. And he gave her no encouragement at all.

". . . there is a danger," he ended, "of which I would, with all kindness and earnestness, warn you. The day dreams in which you habitually indulge are likely to induce a distempered state of mind; and in proportion as all the ordinary uses of the world seem to you flat and unprofitable, you will be unfitted for them without becoming fitted for anything else. Literature cannot be the business of a woman's life, and it ought not to be . . .

"Farewell, Madam. It is not because I have forgotten that I was once young myself, that I write to you in this strain; but because I remember it."

She felt her face burning with shame. She read the letter carefully again and again. At least it was kind of him to answer her at all. It was more than Mr. Wordsworth had troubled to do for Branwell.

She supposed she must write and thank him. Yes, indeed, she must, if only to let him see that she could receive his lesson in the proper spirit. "Without becoming fitted for anything else." The words stung her almost more than the rest of the letter. She would let him know, too, that her "day dreams" as he called them, had never been allowed to stand in the way of her duty.

Indeed, it was late that night before she got a moment to light her bedroom candle and begin another letter.

"I must thank you for the kind and wise advice you have condescended to give me." This time she forced herself to delay her pen until her mind had chosen and formed the sentences properly. "You warn me against the folly of neglecting real duties, for the sake of imaginative pleasures. I am afraid, sir, you think me very foolish. I know the first letter I wrote to you was all senseless trash from beginning to end; but I am not altogether the idle, dreaming being it would seem to denote.

"My father is a clergyman of limited income. I thought it my duty, when I left school, to become a governess. In that capacity I find enough to occupy my thoughts all day long, and my head and hands too, without having a moment's time for one dream of the imagination. In the evenings, I confess I do think, but I never trouble anyone else with my thoughts.

"Once more allow me to thank you with sincere gratitude. I trust I shall never more feel ambitious to see my name in print; if the wish should rise I'll look at Southey's letter and suppress it. It is honour enough for me that I have written to him, and received an answer."

She paused, sighed, and finally signed her name.

Branwell took a studio in Bradford and painted portraits of his friends. Nothing came of his visit to London, where he did not care to stay. Bradford was near enough for him to visit the parsonage fairly often, which delighted the heart of his aunt. She had always preferred this gay, laughing nephew to her nieces, and she tended to spoil him. But Charlotte noticed his growing wildness unhappily. If only Mr. Wordsworth had written and given him some encouragement to work harder at literature, if not at art!

Charlotte had come back home unexpectedly, bringing Anne with her. Anne's health had broken down. Miss

Wooler hadn't understood, and Charlotte had had some sharp words with her headmistress about that. Miss Wooler evidently thought Anne was only pretending ill health. So there had been a painful quarrel when the elder sister defended the younger, and Charlotte had given up her post.

Then one day just before Christmas, Tabby slipped in going down the steep village street and broke her leg. She was brought back to the parsonage groaning with pain. It was obvious that she would be in bed for a long while, and need careful nursing. And the girls had their hands full already.

Miss Branwell knocked on her brother-in-law's study door and entered. He was looking perturbed by the news of Tabby's accident. The magnifying glass he now used to help his eyesight lay untouched on a corner of his desk. He was not even attempting to read.

"Patrick," she said, "this is a busy household. Nursing an invalid would be too much. Don't you agree that Tabby should be sent home until she is better again?"

Mr. Brontë hesitated. "Perhaps. But I scarcely like——"

But Miss Branwell, having been worsted over the geese, was going to have her own way now. "None of us likes," she said briskly, adding, "I have your authority to make arrangements for Tabby to be fetched away?"

He nodded reluctantly and picked up his magnifying glass to indicate that he wished to hear no more on the subject.

When the girls heard the news, they were furious. Turn old Tabby out of the house just because she would make more work for them? *"I'll* talk to Aunt Branwell," exclaimed Charlotte. She ran upstairs in a flash and, for the first time in her life, burst into her aunt's room without knocking.

"Is this true about Tabby? That you mean to send her away?"

Miss Branwell looked from her armchair at her small niece who stood there, fists clenched, panting with indignation and the run up the staircase combined. She stiffened slightly and spoke in a tone of reproof. This time she did not mean to give way.

"No one has any intention of dismissing her, of course. Do control yourself, Charlotte. I may not be able to find anyone to do the work in Tabby's place—none of the young girls is likely to want to leave their homes just at Christmas. We are all busy enough. Impossible to add nursing to the rest of the work to be done."

Charlotte's eyes burned dangerously. "Who else do you think should nurse her?"

"Her family, of course. She has a sister and a niece, and——"

"A sister older than herself, who couldn't possibly lift her or look after her properly! A niece who works all day at the farm near Top Withens and who comes home far too tired to look after anyone but herself!"

"I will not be argued with, Charlotte. And you have left the door open. Tabby can't be moved immediately, of course. But by Wednesday the doctor says he will come with a stretcher, and he has very kindly offered to drive her himself to her sister's cottage."

Charlotte swallowed, trying to calm her voice.

"Aunt, please listen. Tabby has looked after us since we were small. She has taken the part of our mother. When we had measles, she gave up her night's rest to nurse us as well as working by day. We owe her a debt and we don't grudge paying it back."

The small neat figure, so like and yet so unlike Charlotte's own, never moved. The voice said evenly, calmly, "Your sentiments do you credit, my dear. On account of them I shall excuse the extraordinary way you have burst into my room. But Tabby must go till she's better. I am sure she will understand."

Aunt and niece looked at one another for a full second. Then Charlotte said, "Do you really mean this, Aunt? Am I to tell the others you won't change your mind?"

"I really mean it. Recollect that I am in charge of this household, in place of your mother. I must decide what is best. Of course we shall visit poor Tabby and I intend to make some nourishing soup and take it to her myself. It is from a Cornish recipe and far more digestible than your strong Yorkshire broths."

"Soup!" Charlotte's nostrils were pinched with anger. Her voice shook with it again.

"I think you had better go downstairs again before you forget yourself. And be so good as to close the door quietly."

Charlotte marched downstairs to the others and reported: "She won't change her mind. She says Tabby must go."

There was silence. Anne's eyes filled with tears. Then Emily said decisively, "We must *make* her change! We must show her we are in earnest, too."

"But Emily—how?"

"Well, I'm not going to eat a morsel until she gives in. I decided while you were upstairs."

Charlotte nodded approval. "I agree to that. I shall do the same."

"So shall I." Anne's voice sounded as firm as the others.

Emily had cooked the dinner, which was a saddle of mutton with baked potatoes under it and a dish of stewed apples to follow. Mr. Brontë, carving with his usual rapidity, handed the first plate to his sister-in-law. But when he went on to serve his daughters, all three shook their heads like mandarins.

"None today, thank you, Papa."

It was not the family habit to question each other's tastes and doings. Their father ate stolidly through his own mutton. Miss Branwell attempted to do the same. Charlotte, whose turn it was to wait at table, rose and removing the first course, brought in the dish of stewed fruit and the cream and sugar to accompany it. This sort of pudding was usually passed down the table. Again all three girls left their plates empty while offering the dishes to their father and aunt with great politeness.

Miss Branwell rose from table, when she had finished, making no comment whatever.

Supper was the same, except that Mr. Brontë did not join them for that meal, but had his own brought to him on a tray in his study. Miss Branwell ate hers in stony silence, while the three girls again sat before empty plates. But when it came to breakfast time next morning, and Anne (it was her turn) brought through from the kitchen only two bowls of smoking porridge instead of five, she suddenly capitulated.

"Since you are so determined," she said, "then Tabby may stay."

Anne threw her arms round her aunt and kissed her.

Emily shot back into the kitchen to get some more porridge out of the pot for herself and her starving sisters.

Tabby did need a lot of waiting upon. She was apt to be querulous and demanding. But the girls looked after her patiently, remembering all the kindnesses which she herself had shown them when they were small.

Meanwhile Miss Branwell had found a strong young girl called Martha Brown to come and do the hard work. Martha banged about the parsonage in a cheerful fashion, only half-quelled by Tabby's lectures about how to behave in a clergyman's house. She stared in honest amazement after being told not to sing while she swept outside the study door.

"Eh, doant t'parson care for a bit o' a tune?"

CHAPTER *Six*

It was a summer afternoon of the year 1839 as a carriage moved down a pleasant valley. Inside it sat a plump, middle-aged lady with her guest, a pretty young woman, beside her. The pretty young woman was leaning forward eagerly now, since they had almost reached their destination. The sun shone down on her coils of golden hair, and she kept her parasol tilted to preserve the pink and white of her complexion.

This was a different sort of landscape from the wild moors round Haworth. Although the valley was still in Yorkshire, it had lush pastures and woods. The woods had now receded a little, so that both occupants of the carriage could see the house they were making for. It was a large stone mansion set on the slope of the hill.

"I hope we may find Mrs. Sidgwick at home," the older woman remarked, adding kindly, "I can engage her in conversation then, so that you may have a quiet talk with Miss Brontë."

"Thank you, you are very kind. Yes, I *should* like to know if Charlotte is happy here. From her letters, I fancy she isn't."

The carriage turned into the drive and pulled up at

the front door of the house. Before they rang the bell, however, the door burst open and two or three children ran out. They stopped a moment to stare curiously at the visitors, then disappeared in the direction of the woods.

The open door revealed a large and beautifully furnished hall. Turkey carpets lay over the stone flags, heavy carved furniture gleamed with polish, and the lamps lining the walls were of glittering copper or brass. A footman appeared hastily and inquired their names. He led the two ladies across the Turkey carpets, past some glossy oil paintings, then, throwing open the door of the drawing room, announced them.

The lady sitting by the window had already risen to her feet and was halfway across the floor to greet the unknown arrivals. Mrs. Sidgwick had watched the handsome carriage and horses draw up before the front door. They were evidently persons of consequence.

The elder, married, lady to whom the carriage belonged, dropped a curtsey. "Forgive our intrusion, Mrs. Sidgwick. I called to introduce my young friend, Miss Ellen Nussey, who is visiting us. And seeing Stonegappe is only a few miles from my own house, we wondered if it were entirely convenient for her to visit your governess, Miss Brontë?"

A look of surprise crossed the face of the other. She turned to Ellen wonderingly, taking in the expensive clothes, the ringlets, the tiny laced parasol dangling now from her wrist.

"You are—a friend of Miss Brontë's?"

"Since childhood." Ellen replied eagerly. "We were at school together. I should love, if it were possible, to see Charlotte. I'm very fond of her."

"Let me offer you both some tea first."

Mrs. Sidgwick rang the bell and gave orders for tea to be brought in and the visitors' carriage led round to the stables. "Fortunately," she said, "this is Miss Brontë's own tea hour. She is quite at liberty just now. After you have had some refreshment I can take you up to her room."

Ellen's face fell. "Could I not perhaps have tea with her there? We must drive away again shortly and there is so little time——"

She knew she should not have said this, and Mrs. Sidgwick certainly looked a little discomposed. "Very well," she said coldly. "I shall conduct you to Miss Brontë now, and then return to entertain your hostess."

With a slight bow of apology to her other visitor she left the room with Ellen, and led her up a huge staircase with handsome carved banisters, past several closed bedroom doors until she reached one upon which she knocked perfunctorily.

"Come in!"

Yes, it was Charlotte's voice, sounding low and tired. Charlotte sat at a table piled high with household linen laid out for mending. She stared as the door opened, peering a little as if her shortsighted eyes must be deceiving her. Then she jumped up and threw her arms around her friend.

"Ellen, my dearest!"

Mrs. Sidgwick said, "You see I have brought you a pleasant surprise. But Miss Nussey has made quite a journey. Perhaps she would like to wash and tidy a little before tea comes up? The Red Room, if you please. Janet will bring a can of hot water there immediately."

"Oh, thank you, Ma-am!" Charlotte's tone showed real warmth and gratitude. Mrs. Sidgwick looked at her in some surprise. She had never seen her so animated before. Then she glanced at the little tea tray almost hidden behind the piles of linen. It was still untouched. It contained only one cup and saucer, and a meager plate of thin bread and butter. Not at all the sort of tea to offer an elegant creature like Miss Ellen Nussey.

"I shall order another cup, and some cake," Mrs. Sidgwick said hastily, and then withdrew, leaving the friends together.

The Red Room was some distance off, and looked as if it was seldom used. A huge pillared bed stood in the middle of it draped in scarlet damask. An enormous chair covered in a dust sheet loomed whitely beside the bed. The window blinds were drawn down almost completely, filling the room with amber light.

The great cold dressing mirror showed the door opening again slowly behind them. Ellen started, but it was only the housemaid coming in with the hot water. She draped the ewer on the washing stand with fresh towels and withdrew again.

Charlotte waited till she had gone, then burst out, "Oh, Ellen, if you knew how homesick I am! How all this magnificence chills me!"

"But—they are kind to you?"

She shrugged her shoulders. "Oh, yes, I suppose so, in their own way. They sometimes take me visiting with them if there is room in the carriage. We went to Norton Conyers when we were at Harrogate a few weeks ago. Such a strange old house, Ellen!"

"I've heard of it," Ellen had taken off her bonnet and was busily brushing her hair.

"A handsome, shadowy old house, properly furnished

downstairs but upstairs just crammed with the queerest old-fashioned furniture you can imagine! There's a room in it where a mad woman was locked up for years and years, so the housekeeper told us. She took us around as the owner is abroad. But when I asked who the poor woman was, she just said it was an old story and she couldn't remember."

"A good thing, too! You mustn't think of such things, Charlotte, it makes you quite morbid. Let's get back to the nursery again and have tea!"

Mrs. Sidgwick had ordered up a fruit cake, more bread and butter and strawberry jam, in honor of Miss Brontë's visitor. Through the open window came, faintly, the shouts of the playing children.

"You like them?" asked Ellen, digging her small white teeth into a wedge of cake.

Charlotte shrugged her shoulders. "They are completely undisciplined, and I'm not allowed to discipline them. The little boy perhaps—he's only four and has not been quite spoiled yet. And I think he's fond of me, too."

Ellen changed the subject. "The others at home—how are they?"

"Emily is the only one there now, with Papa and Aunt. She's really needed, now that Tabby is growing old. Anne has gone as a governess to a place called Blake Hall, but I don't think she'll stay there long."

"Why?"

"Well, for one thing because Mrs. Ingham, the mother of the children, walked into the nursery suddenly and found that Anne had tied the children to the legs of the table. There are four children, so I mean tied one to each leg—what are you laughing at?"

"If *you* had done such a thing, I could have believed

it. Or, better still, Emily. But Anne! What on earth made her do it?"

"Why, because she wanted some peace to write, of course." Charlotte sounded surprised at the question being even asked.

"I see." Ellen wiped her eyes with her handkerchief and straightened her face. "And I suppose Mrs. Ingham objected?"

"She made a ridiculous fuss. As if children shouldn't be curbed sometimes! But I imagine their mutual patience is wearing thin, and Anne will go back to Haworth quite soon."

"You know, dear, you always said you didn't care for young children, and I'm sure Anne is the same. Your nerves just can't stand their noise. Why don't you look for a position with older girls?"

"Because older girls need to be taught more than I can teach them. Things like music, and French and Italian." Charlotte sighed. "Of course, they would be easier to deal with, but none of us is equipped for it."

Ellen looked out on the velvety lawns with their bright crescents and half-moons of flowers. Everything seemed so peaceful, so—so lush. Was there nothing at Stonegappe that would give Charlotte any enjoyment at all?

"What do you do in the evenings?" she asked suddenly. "Are you always alone?"

"Except when there's a house party. Then I'm invited down to the drawing room, to sit in a corner and admire the fashionable young ladies and their admirers. To clap my hands after they have 'performed' on the piano or the harp. But otherwise, to make myself as inconspicuous as possible."

Ellen felt sorry for the contempt in Charlotte's voice.

But she knew it was no use. Nothing would make the three parsonage girls put aside their shyness and get on with strangers. On a sudden inspiration she said, "Have you ever thought of teaching at home? Having a little school there, I mean?"

Charlotte shook her head. "It would need capital to start, and we haven't any."

"I suppose you wouldn't allow——"

"No, dear, though I'm grateful to you for thinking of it. But we borrow from nobody, not even our greatest friends."

Ellen saw that the shadows were already creeping across the lawns. The carriage would be back before the front door directly. She rose reluctantly.

"And Branwell? What is he doing?"

"He has a studio in Bradford. But I'm afraid the portrait commissions aren't coming along very fast."

"Charlotte, I *do* wish you'd married Henry."

Charlotte gave her rare, enchanting laugh. "Poor Henry! He's far better off with his smart, fashionable wife than he would ever have been with me."

"Yes, but still——"

Ellen sighed again as they went down the staircase together. The drawing-room door opened at the sound of their approach. The two other ladies emerged and all four now moved to the front door, where the carriage was already waiting. The children must have sighted it from the woods, because they were clustered around it. Ellen noticed two pert young girls who stared back at her as she put her foot on the carriage step. A fat little boy rolled near the horses' hoofs, trying to peer at their hocks. Charlotte sprang forward and pulled him back and he turned and put his arms round her neck saying, "I loves you."

The good-bys and speeches of thanks had already been said. But as the carriage moved forward, Ellen distinctly saw the frown that came on Mrs. Sidgwick's face at her offspring's remark and heard, above the crunch of the wheels, the strong Yorkshire voice exclaim, "Love the *governess,* my pet?"

CHAPTER *Seven*

Shortly after this Charlotte gave in her notice to the Sidgwicks. Mrs. Sidgwick received it coldly. Charlotte did not care. She had been too lonely at Stonegappe, too unhappy among people she could not like.

The well-known landscape enfolded her as she approached her home. Instead of the green woodiness of the vale she had just left, here was the windswept moor. Instead of hedges trimmed neatly, the fields on either side of her were now marked off by familiar stone dykes. A strong wind blew on her cheeks. Some people would have winced from it. Charlotte lifted her face to welcome it gratefully.

The gig toiled up the steep village street, past the grim stone houses with their little shops below them; past the Black Bull inn at the corner, and the church and the quiet graveyard, into the lane. There, waiting for her at the parsonage gate, stood her father. She jumped down and kissed him fondly.

To do her honor he joined them at supper that night. Aunt Branwell had made coffee as a treat. Charlotte smelt its fragrance as soon as she entered the parsonage. Coffee instead of the usual cold water! It was an expensive luxury, and had always to be fetched from Keighley as well. Even Mr. Brontë allowed himself a second cup, to celebrate Charlotte's homecoming.

Time passed. The next happening of moment to the inmates of Haworth Parsonage, was the coming of Willie Weightman. The Reverend William Weightman, to give him his full title, was engaged as curate to help Mr. Brontë. He was tall and eager, and very young, and Charlotte liked him immediately, as did the others. He took the position of a new brother to the girls, without in the least usurping the place of Branwell, who was not always at home.

He had a pink and white complexion which made the girls call him "Celia Amelia" to tease him. He teased them back, but would constantly make them little presents or do small kindnesses, and the house was infinitely gayer for his presence.

Charlotte took her place at table to find a bouquet of choice flowers laid at her plate. Willie Weightman watched her with such anxiety to see if the bouquet pleased that she knew at once who had placed it there.

"Thank you. How charming!" She raised the flowers to her nostrils to smell their fragrance.

"They came from old Mrs. Catherick's garden, but I *asked* her before I took them."

They all laughed at the frankness with which he confessed his small robbery. Even Aunt Branwell's little nutcracker face relaxed in a smile. But she looked severe again when Willie, picking up the empty coffeepot, shook it gently to emphasize the fact.

"You won't sleep, any of you, if you drink more coffee tonight," she said firmly.

That would have quelled most people. But Willie

pleaded, "Just one more cup for us all. To celebrate, you know."

"To celebrate what, pray?"

"Anything you like, Ma-am."

"No more beans have been ground."

"I'll grind more, if you permit me."

Miss Branwell hesitated. Perhaps she was remembering that Willie had trudged all the way to Keighley and back to procure the beans for her. Willie, taking her hesitation for consent, snatched up the pot and disappeared toward the kitchen. Sounds from the coffee grinder reached them through the dining-room door which he had left half open. Presently he came back with the coffeepot breathing out fragrant steam in his hand.

The girls were not allowed to roam the moor after sundown. It was a time that Emily in particular liked. The warmth of the day still lingered there, and even after the stars came out, you could see your way through the soft grayness, and hear the trickle of the beck and smell the honey scent of the heath. But the farming folk who lived on the moor were rough and dour, and their dogs, which they let loose at dusk, were even dangerous. It wasn't safe for the three girls to wander about there alone. However, with Celia Amelia for escort, Mr. Brontë withdrew his objection to their strolling out after supper on fine nights. If Charlotte's shortsightedness made her hesitate between path and bog, his strong hand was at her elbow to guide her. But she noticed that he often chose to walk by the side of gentle little Anne.

Willie had a large heart and he gave it away very readily; large pieces of it to different people at once. There was a delightful girl called May who lived at Keighley, and sometimes he came back from there, openly sighing because May had seemed cold. They teased him about the unknown May, and also about another girl called Eleanor who, it appeared, lived in Bradford, and with whom he was conducting a brisk correspondence.

He would come in to dinner, laughing and happy because he had got an amusing letter from Eleanor. Bits of it he read out across the dinner table. It wasn't serious, it was just a game on both sides. It wasn't serious about May either, because he would pretend to measure their curls against hers and anyway, May got engaged to a farmer before the summer was out. Willie bought her a wedding present far too expensive for his small salary and didn't seem the least disturbed.

Was he serious about Anne?

Charlotte dropped a small hint. "He seems to like all girls in the lump, not just one, or even one at a time." She remarked casually to Anne as they were turning out the parlor together. "But of course, he's so open about it, he gives them fair warning."

"Yes, I know," Anne answered gently. Her face and manner were quite impassive. Anne could keep her own counsel, too.

And yet . . .

Surely Willie's eyes sought Anne's even while he took the service for Mr. Brontë; gazing down on the parsonage pew as if he could look at no one but her. Surely Anne's beautiful violet eyes were turned oftener to him than toward anyone else. And his manner was gentler, kinder to her than to anyone else. Besides, he was so very young yet. Presently he would stop playing and grow serious. Or would he, ever?

There was no trouble too great for him to take for the whole Brontë family. Soon Charlotte was to learn of his kindness and self-sacrifice for other people as well. Her shyness kept her from visiting her father's parishioners unless they were really ill or needed her. But presently old Mrs. Catherick fell sick. She was very poor, with a ne'er-do-well son who contributed nothing toward her keep. Charlotte took a shilling or two from her own small store, and a wing of cold chicken, and tapped on the door of the cottage.

Old Mrs. Catherick was not an attractive person to visit. She was rather dirty and her cottage smelled. She was very cross and bad-tempered, too. When Charlotte entered carrying her gifts, the old woman turned her head away.

"I require nawt, Miss Brontë. 'T Curate, he's been and seen to my wants. Grapes he's brought. Look at 'em on the ta-able, and paid the rent too, so's I can die easy in my own bed. Eh, he's a good young man, is Mr. Weightman."

Celia Amelia had said nothing about his constant visits to the old woman. Nor about his efforts to get her son work and keep him comparatively straight. Charlotte began to see there was more behind that lighthearted surface than she had thought. And he got on well with her father, too. He knew how to manage the old man who, up to now, had steadily refused to be "bothered" with help in his pastoral duties.

Yes, if only she could be sure that he was serious about Anne! Because she began to suspect that Anne was serious about him.

She had meant to give herself only one month's enjoyment of home. But now autumn had really come to the moors and she had done nothing whatever about getting a new post. The suggestion Ellen had made that summer afternoon at Stonegappe, must have lain all the while under Charlotte's conscious thoughts. Now it suddenly came to the surface.

She sought out the other two one afternoon, when Willie had gone to Keighley and said abruptly, "I've something to discuss with you. Let's go out on the moor."

It was one of those golden days, as if time chose to stand still before turning round to face winter. The yellow gorse clothed the bare rocks, and the bracken had turned to gold, too. A curlew rose from the path in front of them and spread its wings, crying *Pee-Weet Pee-Weet!* They could see its crest black against the blue sky.

"This way."

Charlotte deliberately led the way across the moor by Emily's own mossy green path. Although nobody could possibly overhear what they said, she felt she wanted their discussion to take place in the most private spot possible. And the most private spot was Emily's favorite hiding place, by the gray pool under the shadow of the rock.

The pool had shrunk in the drought of summer. The little beck leading to it was almost empty so that when at last they looked down on the pool, it seemed farther off from them than usual. The steppingstones were bone dry. The bracken growing about them was brown, not gold. Anne and Charlotte sat down on the stones, but Emily remained standing, suspicious and defiant.

"What is all this about?" she demanded.

Charlotte began breathlessly. "None of us really wants to leave home. Besides you, Emily, are needed here. Or at least, one of us is. So—why not turn the parsonage into a school?"

CHAPTER *Eight*

"Keep a school?"

Emily sounded astonished. Anne's mouth opened slightly.

"Oh, I don't mean a *school* exactly. But if we could find a few older girls to educate here, at home in Haworth, we might earn enough money without having always to live with strangers."

Emily said slowly, "What put that into your head?"

"Ellen did. And you know how practical she is. She'd do her best to find us pupils, I'm sure of that. Just one or two girls who want to finish their education. I'm not fit to keep rowdy little ones in order any more. And neither is Anne."

Anne said, "We haven't room for a school. Not in the parsonage."

Charlotte interrupted her impatiently. "Perhaps I shouldn't have used the word 'school.' I think all Ellen meant was that we should offer to board and teach one or two."

"Where?" Emily asked drily.

"I've thought it all out. We three would have to share

a room, of course. Or perhaps Aunt Branwell would let Anne share hers, and you could take Anne's bed in mine. That would set the little one free. I'm sure parents would pay extra to let their daughter have a room to herself. Then there's the turf room."

"Where would we put the turfs?" Emily asked in a practical way.

"Oh, don't make difficulties, Emily! In the woodshed, of course. Two girls could sleep in the turf room, perhaps three. That would mean four pupils. The parlor would be the schoolroom. Papa and Aunt Branwell never come into it anyway except for meals. And Papa really prefers having a tray in his study. Four girls ought to be enough to——"

Anne said, "You said four young ladies wanting to finish their education. We're really not fit for that, Charlotte. We don't know enough ourselves."

Charlotte was forced to agree. "We can teach them the usual subjects, geography, history and so on. Aunt has taught us to sew. We can all sew well. And why can't we learn the rest ourselves?"

Emily began to tick off the other requisite subjects on her fingers. "Music. Anne can play a few hymn tunes. Drawing, yes. We can all draw. But Italian? And French? We can read French a little, but we can't speak it. There isn't anybody around here who could give us conversation lessons in French. You know that. We've tried to find someone before."

"If two of us learned to speak French fluently, we could do without Italian. And if Anne practiced the piano——"

The evening shadows were beginning to reach the pool. It was getting cold in this shady place. "I've got another idea about learning French. Come, let's go home now. I can tell you on the way."

The brittle fronds of the ferns brushed their skirts as they scrambled onto the path again. They didn't walk along it in single file, now, they were too intent upon hearing Charlotte's idea. They wound their arms round about each others' waists, the two outside ones ploughing their way through the prickly heath.

"Listen," said Charlotte. "You know Aunt always says she will leave us her money?"

They nodded.

"Well—I hate asking for anything. But if I asked her to let us have some *now*——"

"But——"

"She can make it a loan if she likes," Charlotte hurried on. "Then we can pay her back if the scheme prospers. If she would only lend us enough for two of us to go abroad, perhaps to a *pensionnat* in France! We could give English lessons there you know, and receive French ones in return."

The other two were so startled, they stopped dead. Both echoed, "To France!"

"Well," said Charlotte, "we've got to go somewhere to learn to speak French properly. And—and perhaps it wouldn't do us any harm to see a bit of the world."

"If that is so," said Emily firmly, "then you two had better go to France. I'll stay at home and learn to play the piano."

They were now in sight of the back lane leading to the parsonage. Charlotte had sown the seed in their minds. But they would have to wait until they heard of some place suitable. "Not a word to Aunt or Papa as yet," she warned them. "It would be better, first, to know exactly what we are going to do."

"Exactly," said Emily. But her tone was not quite so firm. "You would have to know of a *pensionnat* well spoken of, or you would never be allowed to go. And how are you to find out about one?"

Anne remained silent. She was already in a good post as nursery governess to the children of a Mrs. Robinson who lived near York. This was merely her summer holiday. Although she must leave the parsonage anyway when that was over, it was still possible for her to get home from time to time, to visit Papa and Aunt Branwell, and . . .

And France would be very far away.

Charlotte seemed to be writing a great many letters these days. Especially to her friend Mary Taylor, who had been at school with her and Ellen. Mary was in Brussels, not France. But, of course, they spoke French in Brussels, too.

Anne was packing to go back to teach her pupils, when Charlotte marched into the bedroom strewn with her things, and called Emily in after her.

"I've heard of just the place," she announced. "Mary Taylor has written to me about it. It's the Pensionnat Héger in Brussels."

The other two gaped at her. "But Brussels is in Belgium, not France!"

"What does it matter? We shall learn French there just as well. And we must go to some place personally recommended, if only to satisfy Papa."

"Will you write to this *pensionnat* next?"

Charlotte shook her head. "We must ask his permission first. We can't go further without it. And I must speak to

Aunt, too. It costs a great deal of money even to get there. If she can't lend us the money, then we can't go."

In any case it would be better to have Aunt Branwell on their side. So, that afternoon Charlotte took up her aunt's tea tray, although it was really Emily's turn to do so. As she carried it upstairs her hands shook so much that the delicate china rattled. She would not tell the others, but she was just as terrified of the new plan as they were. Terrified, but determined.

"Come in, my dear!"

Aunt Branwell was sitting, as usual, beside the small fire she insisted upon having, summer as well as winter. She had a shawl over the shoulders too, and the window was firmly shut. Her fringe was still bright auburn-brown, but Charlotte noticed, with a sudden sharp stab of pain and apprehension, how old she had grown.

She laid the tray gently down on the table, and began to pour out a cup from the precious little silver teapot, which, with the fine china, was one of the few relics of former Branwell prosperity.

"May I stay and talk to you while you have your tea, Aunt?"

The old lady nodded. She took a sip of the fragrant tea, then looked shrewdly over the cup at her niece. "You have something on your mind, Charlotte. Tell me what it is."

Charlotte had wondered how to begin. Now the words tumbled out. They all *hated* leaving home. And Ellen had said—had suggested that perhaps—but they weren't properly qualified, even if she and Papa made no objection to having three or four strange girls in the house. . . .

They would have to learn French. And one, at least,

would require to give pianoforte lessons. And if they went abroad, two of them, to this *pensionnat* which was highly recommended, it would cost a good deal, even supposing they could arrange to give English lessons in return for French ones.

Miss Branwell heard her patiently to the end. The eyes under the fringe were bright as a monkey's, alive with intelligence. When Charlotte had stopped and was sitting, miserable, afraid she had not introduced the subject properly or with tact, she very deliberately folded two bits of thin bread and butter together, bit into the sandwich with her shiny false teeth, and then patted the girl with her free hand.

"I think your plan is a good one, my dear. It may prosper or it may not. But I have always wanted my nieces to see more of the world than the little bit enclosed by those cold Yorkshire moors."

Charlotte seized her hand and kissed it impulsively. "Then you don't think me mad?"

The old lady bit into her sandwich again. When she had finished the morsel, she said, "My friends in Cornwall all thought me mad to travel so far as this. But I came because it was my duty to look after my brother-in-law and his motherless children. Don't forget, when I made the journey it was as far and as difficult as the journey to Brussels nowadays."

"And will you take our side with Papa? Will you try to persuade him?"

The old lady's eyes twinkled. "Don't you wish me to do a little more than that?"

Charlotte felt herself blushing hotly. "I should have spoken about the expenses first. Aunt, would you be so *very* kind as to lend us a little capital? There's nobody in the world I would ask except you and Papa, and Papa hasn't any to spare."

"I'll give it to you, my dear. No lending, with a debt tied round your necks from the first. I shall pay the cost of two of you going to Brussels for six months."

The girls never quite knew what Aunt Branwell said to her brother-in-law to make him agree to the scheme. Agree he did, finally. But he kept insisting that one of his "bairns" must be left with him, which of course, was in the plan already. There seemed to be some suspicion in his mind that the third, encouraged by the other two, might leave the family nest as well. It took quite a while to reassure him.

Meanwhile Anne, and Emily, too, began to practice on the piano which was the chief glory of the parsonage with its puckered silk folds above the keyboard and its handsome brass candelholders. Charlotte had no talent for the piano. But it transpired that Celia Amelia had.

"My turn, girls!" He sat down on the stool and began rattling off a catchy air very different from the scales and hymn tunes which came from it from time to time. Mr. Brontë, hearing the unaccustomed sound, opened his study door opposite. Immediately the pianist slowed down his tune to a reverent chant. The study door closed again. Charlotte smothered a laugh and even Emily smiled.

Nobody knew yet, if Emily would go to Brussels with Charlotte. She would not want to go. She had always pined when away from home. But it was impossible for one of them to venture into a strange land alone; and besides, if their little school was ever to be started, two, not just one, must be able to teach French.

And Anne was in a good post already. Before matters were finally fixed, everyone noticed the look of apprehension on Anne's face lest Emily should refuse to go. Even Celia Amelia seemed not quite himself.

Emily asked Charlotte abruptly, "Do you think he is in love with Anne?"

"He loves her, I'm sure. But whether he loves her *best* is another matter."

"Perhaps he would, if he still had opportunities of seeing her from time to time. When Anne comes home for Christmas, for example."

Charlotte went on unpacking the foodstuffs the carrier had brought from Keighley. She must be careful not to urge Emily too much. She must leave things to Emily's good sense and kind heart.

"Neither of us has a post to go to," she said at last. "Anne has. We are free to go abroad, she is not. And besides, Anne needs to be cherished in a home of her own. But he's only twenty-three, Emily. It may be long enough before he can afford to keep a wife."

Emily was staring out of the window, her hands behind her back, like a boy. At last she said, "it seems obvious then, which two of us goes to Brussels. I'll go with you, Charlotte."

PART TWO 1842–1843

Charlotte Abroad

CHAPTER *Nine*

Brussels, one February evening in 1842.

The snow had been falling softly all day. It whitened the towers of the great Cathedral of Sainte Gudule and dimmed the golden carvings of the Guild Houses on the Grande Place. It deadened the passage of the carriages down the Rue Royale, and lay thick in the parks. As soon as footsteps began to mark it, another fall smoothed them over. When the street lamps were lit, the flakes seemed to change from white to gray, battering against the lamps like moths.

A cab was traveling along the Rue d'Isabelle. It stopped at a large house occupying almost half the side of the street. A clergyman got out and walked up to the imposing front door, stooping to read the brass plate just made visible in the light of the street lamp beside it.

PENSIONNAT DES DEMOISELLES, he read, and under that, Madame Héger.

He hurried back to the cab, opened the door and said, "This is the place."

Charlotte and Emily got out. After them came the tall figure of Mr. Brontë himself. The younger of the two men helped the cabman to carry the small trunks up to the front door. He was the English Chaplain in Brussels, with whom Mr. Brontë was to spend that night before he returned forthwith to his Yorkshire moors. Mr. Jenkins, the Chaplain, declined to go in with them, but said he would wait in the cab.

A servant ushered them into a cold, glittering salon, with an enormous white porcelain stove which was obviously unlit, for it gave out no heat whatever. A gilded clock on a bracket chimed nine just as the door opened and Madame Héger came in.

She slid noiselessly toward them like a doll on her heel-less sandals. She was a pretty, plump woman with a soft manner and hard eyes. Mr. Brontë bowed, made a halting speech in the student French he had almost forgotten; the two girls curtseyed. Madame Héger shook hands with them kindly. Then she overwhelmed them with a torrent of French. The three English visitors looked at each other in dismay. But presently grasping the fact that her remarks were only *politesses,* they waited until she had finished speaking. When that happened, Mr. Brontë bowed solemnly again, kissed each of his daughters (they had said their real good-by some time ago), and indicated that he must leave.

Madame Héger went out with him to escort him to the door. Emily cast one wild glance after them and half-rose as if she would run after her father. But she forced herself to sit down again. Charlotte said nothing and made no move. Her face whitened, listening to the retreating footsteps and the final closing of the front door.

They were left alone with their great adventure.

Madame Héger came back and signed to them to follow. They gathered that they were to have some supper, and then she would show them where to sleep. She led them to a smaller, much warmer room, where a round table near the stove was set for two. She pulled the bell rope and an enormously fat woman came in with a tray of food. The woman, who was evidently the cook, wore a series of bunched-out petticoats, a woolen jacket, no stockings on her red legs and wooden sabots on her feet.

The girls, tired and hungry, were confused still further by Madame Héger beginning to speak to this woman in another language, of which they understood not one word. It was far more guttural than French. It was Flemish, to which they would soon get accustomed, hearing it in snatches on the streets, or spoken by the servants of the *pensionnat.*

"Bon appetit!" Madame Héger switched languages again, pointing smilingly at the tray. Then both women left the room.

The supper, though cold, was good. Thin slices of cold meat were dressed with some unknown sauce and served with potato salad. There was a glass dish of baked pears to end with.

Madame Héger re-entered so promptly upon the last spoonful of pear being swallowed, Charlotte had a moment's base suspicion that she had been watching them through the keyhole. She led them up a magnificent staircase, for the school had formerly been a famous convent, through a series of tiny rooms which had once been cells, through the oratory into a much larger room containing five beds, three on one side and two on the other.

Two of the beds were occupied by sleepers already. Madame Héger put a finger to her lips as she passed down the center of the room to its other end, where two of the empty beds faced each other. Charlotte and Emily noticed that their trunks had already been placed at the foot of each. A large chest of drawers with a mirror above it and a ewer and wash basin, stood against the end wall. This they were evidently to share.

Madame Héger laid hands on a large white curtain and drew it halfway across, so that it enclosed their domain turning it into a little room.

"I have heard the English like privacy," she said.

Then she bade them a whispered good night and glided away. The two young sleepers, barely disturbed, muttered and tossed and then grew quiet again. Charlotte and Emily undressed behind the white curtain and got thankfully into bed.

Most of the next day passed like a confused dream. After breakfast, which was only a cup of coffee and a brioche, they went back to make their beds and tidy their corner of the room. The other two girls had done theirs already, Emily and Charlotte having purposely delayed until they were likely to get the room to themselves. But they were not successful after all. For the fifth bed—the bed which had remained empty all night—was occupied now.

It was occupied by a clutter of beautiful clothes flung across the counterpane. By silks and velvets and exquisite little bonnets trimmed with clusters of flowers. The newcomer, unpacking her trunk and humming as she threw each garment carelessly onto the bed, was an equally beautiful girl of about seventeen. She had silky, maize-colored curls, blue eyes without much expression in them, and a skin the transparent tint of a sea shell.

"Oh, hullo!" she greeted them. "You are the two new pupils I suppose? Madame said you were coming."

Charlotte sprang forward and caught a muslin ball dress as it swirled in mid-air. "Oh, you'll crush it! Let me shake it out properly and hang it up for you."

"Thanks." The girl tossed it over to her carelessly. "That's my cupboard over there. I'm sure I ruin all my clothes, I simply can't treat them properly. It's a shame, isn't it?"

"Yes," said Emily dryly.

"You wouldn't like to iron some of my dresses, if you've a moment?"

"No, thank you."

The girl didn't look the least offended. "My name's Maria Miller. You are the Miss Brontës, aren't you? Have you ever been abroad before?"

She had picked up one of her bonnets from the bed and handed it to Charlotte while she spoke. Charlotte hesitated, then took the bonnet and placed it tidily on the shelf of the cupboard.

"This is the first time we have crossed the Channel," she said.

"Oh, how charming!" exclaimed Maria. "I quite envy you the novelty. First impressions, you know. I've made so many crossings, I've quite forgotten my first one. I'm *blasée* now about travel."

Charlotte burst out laughing. Even Emily smiled.

"Why are you laughing at me?" Maria's good temper seemed ruffled for the first time.

"Because you're too young to be *blasée* about anything."

"I'm seventeen."

"You only look sixteen. Are you studying here?"

Maria nodded. "I was out at a dance last night, so Madame let me stay with my friends till this morning. Term's only just begun you know. Not that I'm likely to learn anything more than I have already."

Emily said quite seriously, "That's a pity."

"Oh, I can do some things very well, I assure you! I can sing and play beautifully. I suppose I speak French well enough, one has to if one enjoys any social life here. I go out quite a lot. Madame Héger can't stop me when my godfather says I may. He pays the bills."

She kept handing articles of clothing to Charlotte to tidy away as she spoke. Presently Charlotte stopped taking them and said, with her hands behind her back, "I'm not your maid, Maria. You must unpack for yourself."

"Well, you'd have been a fool to go on," Maria said calmly, adding, "Wait for me a few seconds. Then I can go downstairs with you and introduce you to the others."

When the last article from her trunk had been hastily pushed into the now-gaping cupboard, Maria held out her hands to them with a pretty gesture. "Come along now. The staircase is wide enough for us to go down together."

They had almost reached the bottom of the staircase when a man crossed the hall with quick, nervous steps. He was short and slim, and when he looked up at them, Charlotte saw he had a handsome face alive with intelligence. He gave a brief bow, then disappeared into Madame Héger's private sitting room.

"Who is that?" asked Charlotte quickly.

"Monsieur Héger of course! He teaches at the Athénée College, but he gives lectures to us as well. He's so good, I really believe he may knock something into my head someday."

CHAPTER *Ten*

Madame Héger's school smelt of furniture polish and scent. First thing in the morning, Pierre, the morose husband of the fat cook, would slide over the floors in felt overboots, rubbing in the polish plentifully smeared upon the parquet. The Brontë girls never used scent; only Aunt Branwell would sometimes put a drop or two of *eau de Cologne* on her handkerchief. Emily wrinkled up her nose disdainfully as some of the older pupils belonging to Class Four, happened to pass by.

Neither she nor Charlotte liked the girls of Class Four. They were the oldest group and thought themselves women of the world already. According to Charlotte, who wrote home about them, it was a world of deceit, showy riches and bold impertinence. The girls of Class Four would stare at the two shabbily dressed newcomers, then shrug their shoulders and titter. According to Charlotte again, they had no manners at all. But then they were foreigners and she had never lived among foreigners before.

Other things were strange, besides the girls of Class Four. For instance, supper was much, much later than at home. And now and then, Madame Héger allowed a few favored pupils to dine later still, if she thought fit to take them to the theater or the opera.

Madame Héger thought it educative to take small parties of her girls to such things. On one occasion they saw an amusing opera, Rossini's *Barber of Seville.* The music tinkled along, the costumed singers made their entries and exits, and Monsieur Héger kindly distributed bonbons between the acts.

But the piece did not stir the Brontë girls. It was a comedy of manners. They could not appreciate its polish; they disdained its trifling. Still, such outings helped to break the monotony of school life which enfolded them again, once the strangeness had begun to wear off.

Madame Héger's school had twelve boarders and forty day girls. Three women teachers lived in it. One Englishwoman, a Miss Dawson, visited to give English lessons to the difficult girls of Class Four. Charlotte pitied her. As well as these, visiting masters came to teach drawing, music and so on. Emily and Charlotte knew only a little schoolgirl French. They were determined to know more, and they had only six months to do it in. They were far older than the other pupils. They studied hard.

They enjoyed Monsieur Héger's class best, in spite of the fact that he was intensely irritable and would fly at them if they made a mistake. Then his delicate features would become contorted, he would even brandish his fists at them. But he had his own original ways of teaching. He could be sympathetic and kind. They preferred him to the placid automaton that was his wife.

"Miss Charlotte," he demanded one day. "How is it that your compositions are always so much better than your translations?"

"Because I prefer to compose," Charlotte answered quietly.

"Yes, yes. You prefer to use your imagination. But imagination must have its feet touching the ground before its wings can unfurl. Take that last composition of yours for example. You imagine a being standing on top of a high mountain, looking down on a sunlit valley. Through the valley come dancing figures. Young men and maidens. Very nice. Very pretty. They appear to be singing, too."

"Yes, Monsieur?"

He put his dark head on one side, looking at her. "The singing is all right, one might hear it perhaps if one were not too far up the mountain. But the garlands the nymphs are wearing? Could you really observe them from that height?"

Charlotte's face quivered. She had made a mistake. A bad mistake.

He said more kindly, "You have a great faculty of invention. Someday perhaps— But you must always remember to avoid writing down the impossible."

"Yes, Monsieur. I see that now."

He paused, thinking; tapping his nervous fingers on the edge of his desk. "I have an idea. Instead of tormenting you and Miss Emily with grammar and dictionary, I bid you throw away the latter and cease troubling about the former. You will instead, translate some of our finest French prose. You have taste and an ear for words. If you fall into the proper rhythm of the prose, the right words will come."

It was even more difficult without the dictionary, but Monsieur Héger showed that he meant what he said, for he frowned most terribly if he found one lying on their desks. And meanwhile, during their daily life they were unconsciously picking up words as well as the right accent. As for the translations, he gave them the classics with their pure elegance of form.

Both the sisters found that their English as well as their French, was gaining in clarity and ease. But Emily did not get on with the master as well as Charlotte. Once in class, she contradicted him flatly.

"I want you young ladies to listen to my reading of one of our most admired authors, the Abbé Bossuet," he said one day. "Then when you write your compositions, you can copy the style of some of the finest prose ever written."

Emily stood up and said, "Why?"

Monsieur Héger's bushy black eyebrows rose into his forehead. "Why not, Mademoiselle?"

"I think," said Emily, speaking as carefully and politely as she could, "that it would be bad for any of us with a taste for writing to copy any style but our own."

Maria Miller turned round and giggled. The rest of the class watched Monsieur, agape.

He asked equally politely, "Do you, Mademoiselle, intend to write professionally yourself, although, of course, in finer style than the Abbé?"

Emily answered composedly, "If I did, I could never model myself on anyone else. I would have to write as I choose."

"And you, Miss Charlotte?"

"I'm afraid I agree with my sister. But as you order us to do so, I shall do my best."

After the class, Charlotte sought out Emily. Her dream

of writing had awakened again. She could not quench it. "Why did you bring me back to the old days when we scribbled so happily—so wastefully?" she asked.

"Because I couldn't help it. *You* know that that's what we really want to do."

Charlotte remembered Southey's letter and sighed. "I've put that dream behind me," she said. "I must concentrate on preparing for our school."

"You may put it behind you," Emily told her. "But it will always be there."

Indeed, Charlotte worked so hard at her French, she had scarcely a moment for anything else, even for writing home. They both lived for the letters that came from the parsonage. They both searched Anne's letters for any allusions to Celia Amelia, but if she mentioned him, it was almost casually, to tell of yet another new flame of his, and then, sometimes, to report that the flame was now cold ashes.

There was the usual outbreak of fever at Haworth that spring. The cottages had no plumbing and the land was poorly drained. Miss Branwell wrote that Willie Weightman was indefatigable in visiting the sick and doing all he could to help them. "It is, indeed, fortunate," she wrote, "that your Father has such a conscientious assistant, for with his bad sight and poor health, he can hardly do as much as he used to in that direction."

Spring was coming to Brussels, too. A fine garden lay behind the *pensionnat* with a long arbor covered with vines. The arbor would soon be domed in green. The snow had been swept from the parks, and as the sisters hurried through the streets to the post or merely to get a little fresh air before their evening study, the cafés had opened their doors for air, and the smell of cigar smoke and beer floated out as they passed.

It was a city of bells. The metallic clang of the nearby church of St. Jean broke their days into sections; and if they walked far enough, the deep bells of Sainte Gudule seemed to shatter the air. Charlotte was happy. This was a new life, as strange as anything she and Branwell had ever written about in their imaginary country of Angria. She stored up everything, everything in her memory. Who knew when it might be useful?

Yet they kept together and made few friends. The plump Belgian girls thought them "odd" and their clothes shabby and lacking in chic. Most of them were rich and despised the daughters of a poor Protestant pastor. Not that Charlotte and Emily cared.

Only Maria Miller chattered and was friendly, but then her bed was next to theirs, and she often kept them from sleeping by recounting her adventures with her admirers. She went out a great deal to the houses of friends. She spoke often about a young man called Isadore, who seemed to be the favorite of the moment. Charlotte listened politely. Emily went to sleep.

Their bedroom door had a pane of glass let into it, with an almost transparent curtain hanging before it. Sometimes Charlotte imagined she saw a dark shadow behind the curtain; sometimes a pinprick of light showed through after dark, as if someone stood there, candle in hand.

"Oh, that's only Madame listening," Maria said offhandedly. "She creeps about and listens everywhere; they do that in foreign schools, you know. It is called *La Surveillance.*"

Charlotte was shocked and said so. Maria only laughed.

"So long as I remember to talk about Isadore in English, she won't understand a word, so what does it matter?"

Madame Héger certainly had a habit of appearing silently, in those heel-less shoes of hers. Now that it was warmer, and some of the Belgian girls would sit chattering in the arbor, Charlotte or Emily would catch sight of her plump, neat figure flitting behind the leaves. Listening. Always listening.

"They don't even mind it!" Emily would exclaim indignantly.

"They're used to it," Charlotte would say, adding, "From what I've seen of them they couldn't be trusted anyway."

For a little while there was no letter from home. Then Aunt Branwell wrote. Even before the words of the letter penetrated, Charlotte noticed, not for the first time, how trembly the old lady's handwriting had become.

"What is the matter?" Emily asked, seeing her face.

"Willie Weightman is dead."

She handed the letter over to Emily who read it. Gay, lighthearted Celia Amelia had given his own life in nursing a sick child whose parents had both died of the fever. All that day they couldn't believe it.

They waited to hear from Anne. When she did write at last, it was composedly, speaking of his death merely as that of someone who had been a good friend to them all. No more.

"I wonder——" Emily said, folding the letter up.

Charlotte said, "I don't suppose we shall ever know."

It was autumn now. The chestnut trees on the avenues were dropping their leaves and sometimes a cold little wind blew through the park. It brought them news of another death. Aunt Branwell's.

The sisters asked permission to go home at once. Both Monsieur and Madame Héger were sympathetic, but to Charlotte's ear Madame's speech of condolence rang false beside her husband's real feeling and warmth of words. More and more Charlotte turned for support to Constantin Héger. More and more she felt that his wife resented the sympathy between them, drawing herself coldly away from the two English girls. Monsieur Héger escorted them on the first stage of their journey home. His was the last face Charlotte saw as they started on the long journey toward the coast.

CHAPTER *Eleven*

Aunt Branwell's room was now free and empty. Her faded water colors still hung on the walls, her armchair still stood beside the fireplace. The girls felt a pang each time they looked in. None of them liked to even mention the fact that the room would be useful for pupils if ever they got their little school going. She had left them each three hundred pounds. That would be useful, too. But they missed the old lady, especially Branwell, whom she had always spoiled. He had come home for the funeral, but his spirits and laughter were quenched.

Presently Anne went back to her post as governess to the Robinson children. Since Mrs. Robinson had a son the right age, Branwell was also engaged to go there as tutor. Anne looked forward to returning to her post more happily than she usually did, for she would have her beloved brother with her this time.

One day Emily came back from a walk on the moors with a huge fierce dog, half mastiff, half bull terrier, lurching after her. She gave no explanation at first, merely led him to the kitchen and fed him with hunks of meat before the frightened eyes of Martha, who lived with them permanently now. Aunt Branwell had disliked dogs and always forbidden them in the house. Emily had always wanted one. But such a dog!

When the brute was fed, Emily explained. She had met a farmer out on the moor with his gun and the dog. The dog was to be shot. He wouldn't take orders. If punished, he flew at the punisher. Emily said the dog knew. "He knew as well as either of us did. He was trembling. He looked at me. I said I would take him. That's all."

The dog stood there in the middle of the kitchen floor, listening. Charlotte stepped forward and laid her hand timidly on the great beast's head. He turned sideways to lick it.

"You see?" cried Emily triumphantly.

Martha had prudently retired to the scullery. Now she peeped out. " 'T beast seems quiet enough," she exclaimed.

"Of course he is if he's treated kindly. Even the man said that. He said there's no vice in him, but he won't be brooked. And there are children up at the farm who maul him about."

Charlotte said, "We must ask Papa if we can keep him."

Mr. Brontë himself was without fear, and he knew his daughter Emily's power over animals. Rather to their surprise he consented. Perhaps it was because the old, lawless days of long ago on the moors still stayed in his mind. The household needed protection. Hitherto he had been ready to do that with his own pistol. Now he could scarcely see to fire it.

Emily called her dog Keeper. He was devoted to her and made no trouble. But then nobody tried the experiment of crossing him, though he would generally obey Emily's commands out of affection. All except one. The parsonage was kept immaculately clean, and each of the beds was covered with a snow-white counterpane. But Keeper loved to lie on a bed. Threats, commands from the rest of the family, failed to get him down from the particular one he had chosen. Sometimes he would clamber down sulkily for Emily's sake. But that wasn't enough.

"He *must* learn not to jump up in the first place," Emily herself said, looking at muddy paw marks and loose hairs on her own honeycomb quilt.

It was Martha who had called her up to see the damage. Keeper wasn't there. He had jumped down of his own sweet will sometime before. He was now lying before the open front door, watching the sparrows on the grass.

Emily put two fingers to her mouth and whistled. Keeper always obeyed that piercing call, which nobody else could make but herself. He came lumbering upstairs in search of her. But when he saw where she was, he stopped in the doorway, bristling.

"Eh, but 'e knows fine enough!" Martha exclaimed.

Emily pointed to the bed and spoke sternly. For once Keeper did not choose to listen to her. He gave her a wicked look, very different from the affectionate ones he generally bestowed on his mistress, and turning walked downstairs again.

"Say what you like Miss Em'ly, but yon dog should 'a been shot. So 't should. I've more in this house to do than wash counterpanes all day long."

"You won't have to," Emily told her calmly, "or perhaps, just once more. By that time he will have learned his lesson."

"What will ye do if 'e goes up again?"

"I shall thrash him."

"But, Miss Em'ly that be dangerous! Farmer said——"

"I know what he said. But Keeper must be made to obey. It's no use punishing him now, when he's off the bed and downstairs already. He must be caught lying on one of them so that he fully understands what he's done."

The wait was like the brooding pause before a storm breaks. Everyone knew what Emily meant to do. No one could stop her. Charlotte was terrified. She went upstairs several times a day to make sure all the bedroom doors were closed.

But it was Martha who found him out in the end. It was one evening just after supper. Mr. Brontë had gone to his study. The girls were trying to keep up their French by reading to one another from one of the books Monsieur Héger had given them. Martha tapped on the parlor door and then came in, trembling with delighted anticipation.

"Miss Emily! Keeper be on Master's bed!"

Emily had been reading. She closed the book quietly and began to go out of the room. Charlotte caught at her imploringly. "Please, please don't risk it! I'll wash the counterpane tomorrow. Martha needn't trouble."

Emily twitched her skirt out of her sister's grasp and walked steadily out of the room and upstairs. Charlotte and Martha stood in the open doorway, watching. Presently a scuffle was heard and a low growling. Emily reappeared, her hand twisted in Keeper's collar so that he could not turn round and snap at her. So, she had pounced, and hauled him off the bed. So, she must continue to hold him if he was not to spring at her throat.

Their progress down the staircase was slow. Emily was bent sideways, restraining the dog who, resisting, sat back with his full weight against every step. There was no question but that he knew what he had done. Charlotte held her breath, watching. What would Emily do when they reached the bottom stair?

Emily dared not increase the gap between herself and Keeper or he would spring. There was no time to seize the little whip which hung, uselessly, near the front door. It was too far off. The others saw her drop suddenly to her knees, still holding on to Keeper's collar with one hand while she beat him about the head and eyes with the closed fist of the other.

He could not get away from her hard punishment. Half blinded and wholly quelled, he let her lead him away at the finish to bathe his eyes and console him. She soothed the bruises with warm water. Though whimpering with pain, he laid his big head on her knee, thankful for what she was doing. And when Charlotte followed them into the kitchen she saw tears were pouring down Emily's face.

"Oh, how I hated doing it!" she said.

Keeper never jumped up on a bed again.

A few weeks after Miss Branwell's death they had a visit from Ellen Nussey. After some thought, the girls prepared their aunt's room for her. Aunt Branwell had loved Ellen; the room could not remain unused forever, that would be morbid, so Ellen should be the first to occupy it.

She was the same as ever, a little plumper, a little older, but so pretty that Charlotte, who secretly felt her plainness beside the good looks of her friend, could not understand why some rich suitor hadn't snatched her up already. However, Ellen seemed very happy as she was. The two girls renewed their long walks together. Emily, as always, preferred to take her walks alone.

It had been a wetter summer than usual. Now it was

winter and the beck gushed in torrents over the moors. Silvery threads of waterfalls dropped into it farther up in the hills. If you stood still, you could hear their faint tinkling like breaking glass.

"Charlotte," said Ellen, half-turning on the narrow path to address the other as they walked home late one afternoon, "what about the school? You know I'm ready to help you all I can."

Charlotte didn't answer for a moment or two. Then she said slowly, "We haven't been able to think—to make any plans as yet. I for one would be glad to delay things for another half-year, and Emily feels the same. Anne is earning money which would be useful, too."

Ellen shrugged her plump shoulders. *"Why* do you want to delay?"

For answer Charlotte drew a letter out of her pocket and handed it to Ellen who glanced at the foreign stamp, the spidery writing, the Brussels postmark and laughed. "You'd better translate. My French won't be equal to it."

"It's from Madame Héger. She writes suggesting that I should return to the *pensionnat,* this time on a small salary. I'm to get my board and some tuition as well, in return for taking a few classes."

"But why delay? What more can you learn that you don't know already?"

"It is the classes in form and composition that I am tempted by. The classes given by Monsieur Héger. They stimulate my mind. They've quite reformed my own writing; I don't even want to use such flowery imagery as I used to."

Ellen looked back quickly at her. "So you still want to write?"

Charlotte said sadly, "I *want* to, of course. But—I was told once by someone whose opinion I greatly respect, to put that dream out of my mind. Still, there's no harm, is there, in learning how to put down things clearly on paper?"

CHAPTER *Twelve*

The first of the *pensionnat* pupils Charlotte met on arrival was Maria Miller. She came waltzing downstairs to meet her, and flung her arms affectionately round her neck.

"How charming to see you again, dear Miss Brontë! Do you know, I'm in your sister Emily's bed now, so we shall be quite cosy and private at the end of the dormitory, away from the other horrid girls!"

Pierre, the man-of-all-work, who had gone ahead up the staircase with Charlotte's trunk on his shoulder, looked back crossly, wanting her to follow. He expected a small tip for the service, and Charlotte gave it to him after he had banged her trunk down on the floor of the bedroom.

"Sale bête!" Maria, who had followed her upstairs again, added, "Those Flemish are such coarse brutes, don't you think? How they can belong to the same race as—as Isadore, I can't imagine!"

"So that little flirt continues?"

"How do you know it isn't a grand passion? But, of course, you wouldn't——"

Charlotte flushed angrily and bent over the lid of her trunk. So Maria, too, thought her just a small, plain little shadow unable to feel, or evoke, any passion? Then the thought of the lightheaded Maria feeling anything but interest in herself made her smile again. It was Maria who wouldn't recognize a grand passion when she saw it; she was incapable of so much feeling.

"You've come back to teach, haven't you? I hear Mr. Wilson, the English visiting master has left. Heaven help you, if you have to take his class!"

"Why?" Her heart sank.

"Oh, those great hulking Flamandes have quite a reputation for insolence. You remember Miss Dawson? They broke her nerve, you know, in two months."

Charlotte's heart sank still further. She did, indeed, remember Miss Dawson, who had private pupils in Brussels, and who visited the *pensionnat* to take a class there. That class! Now she recollected encountering the poor woman hurrying out one day, her face streaming with tears. Mr. Wilson had taken her place, and now he, too, had left.

"And you're such a little thing, you'll never quell them," Maria offered, swinging on the iron bedpost nearest her. She said it casually, lightly. For the moment Charlotte hated her. Then she told herself that at least Maria was not cruel or malicious. As well blame a butterfly for landing on a flower!

Next morning Madame Héger summoned her to her own cosy parlor, not the cold salon used only for the reception and impressing of parents.

"You feel rested after your journey, Miss Charlotte? Able to take a class?"

"Yes, Madame."

"Then perhaps you will kindly give Class Four some English dictation this morning."

It was the class Maria had warned her about. Charlotte opened her mouth, then caught Madame's eyes watching her keenly, watching to see if she would flinch. She would not flinch.

"Certainly, Madame."

There was a gleam of approval in those bright sharp eyes. But Madame Héger had lowered them again as she rose and moved toward the door.

"Come then, and I will introduce you. They are, as you know, the oldest pupils in the school, so they will profit most. I believe they had been set a holiday task in English composition, before Mr. Wilson—left. No doubt you will wish to correct these first."

Charlotte's heart was thumping in her breast. When here herself as a pupil, she had avoided the company of the coarse, loud-mouthed girls who composed Class Four. Now she must teach them. Must quell them somehow.

They sat waiting in the classroom, deceptively silent. They listened politely to Madame's little speech of introduction. They waited until she was, presumably, out of earshot again. Then they broke out. They did not even pretend to listen to Charlotte's own little speech of welcome. They turned contemptuously from her and talked loudly among themselves. She tried to raise her voice against the hubbub, but it was of no use. She knew the girls were doing this on purpose; that they intended to break her as they had broken poor Miss Dawson.

Three of them sat in the front row, just under her desk. Blanche, Rose, and Louise, three girls of sixteen to eighteen, from wealthy Brussels families. Richly dressed, nonchalant, scornful of the poor little English governess who was only a Protestant pastor's daughter, they talked loudly to each other, bursting out into laughter at times which she knew was directed at her.

Yet she knew, too, that they were not the worst. They were great stupid lumps, with not enough intelligence between them to conduct such a deliberate campaign. They were following orders from the ringleader, Marie Celeste. Marie Celeste, quiet-seeming, but far more malicious, had always led them in their campaigns. Even Madame Héger knew that.

It was Madame Héger herself who had said once to Emily, "She it is who manufactures the bombs. The others, they only fire them."

Charlotte was too shortsighted to see where Marie Celeste was sitting. But something had to be done quickly to conquer the three immediately before her. Words were not sufficient. They were determined to make too much noise to hear hers, in any case. She must act.

They sat with their English compositions before them. They had expected her to ask for the papers to be handed up, so that she could read them aloud and criticize. Instead, she deliberately stepped down from her small platform, picked up that of the nearest girl, Rose, and stood quietly reading it as if quite indifferent to the noise. Then, with a look of scorn on her face, she tore the pages across and dropped them in the wastepaper basket.

Her contempt pierced their hides as nothing else would have done. Rose flushed crimson with mortification. Her friends fell silent. In the momentary hush that followed the unexpected action, Charlotte's voice could be clearly heard.

"I shall now collect the other compositions. If they

are no better than Mademoiselle Rose's, they will be scarcely worth reading."

Like all the doors of the *pensionnat,* the one to the classroom had a pane of glass, and a thin curtain before it. In passing it, Charlotte noticed a shadow standing, motionless in the passage behind the curtain. Madame Héger had not gone far. She was exercising *La Surveillance* now.

Charlotte walked slowly between the desks. The girls were so busy watching to see what she would do next, that for the moment they had dropped their tormenting tactics. She took care to look as if she had no other purpose than to collect the written sheets lying before them. But she had. She was looking for Marie Celeste.

At the back of the classroom there was a door, which as usual was ajar. It led into a small room used to store extra desks and classroom furniture. Marie Celeste sat with her back to the door, leaning nonchalantly against the wall beside it. As Charlotte approached, she said something clearly, but in Flemish, which the English girl could not understand. She could understand its meaning, however, for the mocking laughter burst out again immediately. The others, taking courage, would follow Marie Celeste's cue. There would be no peace until Marie Celeste was silenced.

Charlotte took a few steps more. She walked carelessly, putting out her hand to right and left, to pick up the compositions. But she was measuring Marie Celeste with her eye. The girl was small and slight, almost as small as herself. And if taken suddenly by surprise . . .

She cast a quick glance at the door behind her to make sure its key was still in the lock. Then she leaned suddenly toward her tormentor, as if to take up the composition, lying on the desk, but instead, she seized her suddenly by the shoulder, pushed her into the little storeroom and turned the key in the lock.

A gasp rose up from the class. It was a delighted gasp, since Marie Celeste, for all her power over them, was not really popular. Charlotte walked back to her own desk, this time amid an attentive silence.

"I shall not trouble to criticize your efforts," she told them clearly, "for holiday tasks are generally not worth consideration. I shall, instead, read you a piece of English prose. You will write out a précis of it for the next class."

She glanced toward the other door, the glass one, as she spoke. The shadow was moving away. Madame had satisfied herself that Mademoiselle Brontë could handle the Fourth Class. From then onward, she had no more trouble. Pleadings, requests, would have had no effect on such girls. Only forcible actions they could understand. They could even admire them.

Charlotte grew to look forward to Monsieur Héger's own lessons with an impatience which made the rest of the week seem long. Yes, even though he would burst with rage because she did not always agree with his point of view.

"Ah, you think Constantin Héger has a bee in his bonnet about style? You listen so demurely, the hands folded, but inwardly you think 'Poor Monsieur Héger, he lacks the imagination, the fire, in himself! He thinks mere accurate observation more important than romantic flights of fancy!' "

"You are wrong, Monsieur," Charlotte would say calmly, hands still folded, "I would never say you lack fire."

Then the dark face would soften, the glance grow kindly. "I speak thus for your own sake. This essay of yours now. It is supposed to be a dream, hein?"

"If you choose, Monsieur."

"I call it a nightmare of fantasy. Beware too much fantasy! The reader must always be led up to it gently, not plunged into it as into a caldron of boiling oil!"

And then he would go away, and come back with two cups of steaming coffee and two delicious crisp brioches, just in case her feelings had been really hurt.

So, insensibly, she was led to avoid the wild language in which they had all clothed their stories of Angria long ago in the parsonage. And he would criticize more gently, encouraging her to observe nature and to put it down as clearly as she could. It was wonderful practice for what was to come.

CHAPTER *Thirteen*

Now it was summer. In the garden behind the *pensionnat* the orange trees flowered and scented the air. The long arbor darkened as its vines sprawled overhead, letting through mere flecks of sunshine. The girls were allowed to take out their supper of fruit and bread and eat it there. Only Charlotte paced up and down, lonely, longing now for home.

Everyone else had friends' houses to go to on Sundays and holidays. Madame Héger was especially lenient with Maria because she had a rich godfather, who paid lavishly for "extras." She would allow her to attend dances and come in later than the others. Many nights, Charlotte would be wakened up from her first sleep by Maria coming in carelessly and sitting down on the end of her bed, to chatter about her various "conquests."

One of them was a young English doctor called John. He had come to Brussels for some advanced study in medicine, and was living with the family of the British Chaplain, Mr. Jenkins. The Jenkins family did ask Charlotte sometimes to their home for Sunday-night supper, but conversation there was on the dull side, and only the presence of John enlivened the atmosphere. He reminded Charlotte a little of Willie Weightman, except that he was more solemn and shy. He called indefatigably at the *pensionnat* but not to see her, to see Maria. His people and hers were acquainted over in England. This irked Maria, because she could find no excuse for avoiding him.

"*Toute même,* he would make her a very suitable husband." Madame Héger, mending linen beside Charlotte, bit off a thread. "He is, for one thing, utterly devoted. For another, he is a Protestant. And for a third, Monsieur Jenkins tells me he hopes to inherit from a rich uncle."

Charlotte bent her head over a sheet. She did not think John stood the slightest chance against the fascinating Isadore. However, she teased Maria a little, after they had gone to bed. The other girls were snoring already and appeared undisturbed by their whispered conversation.

"John?" Maria shrugged her shoulders under the beribboned nightgown. "Oh, he's all right as an escort, and to get bouquets and chocolates from. But he's so dull! Not like——"

"Not like Isadore," put in Charlotte slyly.

"Isadore?" There was a note of real surprise in her tones. Then she pulled herself together quickly. "Oh, yes, of course. Not in the least like Isadore."

Charlotte watched Maria jump into bed, curl round like a kitten and pull the bedclothes, as usual right over her head except for a hole for breathing and a bright curl or two showing against the pillow. I'm quite sure she wasn't going to say Isadore first, she reflected as she blew out the candle.

It came the time for the holidays. To save the expense of traveling to England and back, Madame Héger had said

Charlotte could remain in the house after the other pupils had left. Maria was going to do the same. Her rich godfather, who generally took her to delightful places like the Riviera, was ill and could not do so this year, and her own father, a poor officer on half-pay, could not afford unnecessary traveling expenses any more than Charlotte could.

"I am glad, Miss Charlotte, that you will be here with Maria. That type needs to be closely watched."

Charlotte had grown accustomed to this attitude, but she hated it and only said coldly, "Maria has so many invitations to go to other peoples' houses, she is not likely to be here very much. And I think, Madame, that you do not trouble yourself about where she goes?"

"Naturally not," Madame looked mildly surprised. "I know who invite her, for they must write to me first. They are all of the highest rank in our Brussels society. When she is with them, they must take responsibility. When she is under my roof, I must."

It became insufferably hot in the city. Charlotte was driven, during the day, from the baking heat of the garden to the cool great rooms of the *pensionnat*. Empty of pupils, they seemed larger than ever. Now only her footsteps echoed over the polished floor. Monsieur Héger was often in the country on business. Madame would sit and hold her coffee parties with her friends, in the white and gold salon this time because, though it was too cold in winter, it was now deliciously cool.

The Jenkins family had gone to the coast. Maria was often out at gay picnic parties, when (as she told Charlotte when she came back) two or even three carriages of the guests would drive out to the woods beyond Brussels and eat cold food under the trees.

"Though Alfred is *most* particular that I don't sit down on any place damp."

"Alfred?"

"Oh—I meant Isadore, of course. How stupid you are, dear Miss Brontë!"

Charlotte was a little uneasy. If Maria had dropped Isadore and was now interested in somebody else, why didn't she say so? Why pretend that she had made a slip of the tongue when Charlotte was sure she hadn't?

One day the house seemed emptier than usual. Even indoors it was warm, for the sunlight struck through the cracks of the wooden shutters fastened over the windows in a vain attempt to keep it out. Through the closed doors of the salon came the murmur of conversation. Madame Héger was giving one of her coffee parties. It struck Charlotte with a pang that she might have been included, too.

Maria had gone out as usual. The carriage of her friends, the De Bassompierres, had come for her just after lunch. They were going to drive to the park. Charlotte watched her run happily down the staircase in a light muslin dress trimmed with cherry-colored ribbons, swinging her bonnet in her hand. Then the great front door had slammed behind her and the house fell dreadfully silent again.

Charlotte went slowly into one of the deserted classrooms. She sat down to write a letter to Emily. But when she read over the first page, she saw that her loneliness had seeped in to it. That would not do. She mustn't let them think, at home, she was miserable. She closed her writing case again. Better get the letter done after something had happened to raise her spirits. But what?

She would go out and take a walk through the city.

No, she would take her book and sit in the park. Its green coolness beckoned her even in thought. She would be alone there still, yet not quite alone. There would be children to watch, playing under the trees. Perhaps, too, the band would be playing. The park was so vast, there was little chance, surely, of running into Maria with her friends. And if she did, was it not common ground to everybody?

She fetched her bonnet and let herself quietly out of the house. The cobblestones of the Rue d'Isabelle struck hot through the soles of her feet. When she got to the end of it, she saw the pale cloud of summer dust lying over the Old Town. Never mind, once through that cloud, she would be in the shade of the park. Sitting there, cool and quiet, with her book on her knee.

No carriages might enter the park. They stood lined up at its entrance. Charlotte joined the parties of strollers walking up the broad central walk. She paused, like them, to refresh herself with the sight of the jets of cool water spouting into the stone basin at the end of it. Then she turned aside to lose herself among the huge chestnuts whose blossoms had long since browned and fallen. She sat down on a rustic seat at the base of one of them and leaned her head against its trunk.

She must have fallen into a doze, for the sound of voices woke her up suddenly. Her book had slipped from her lap to the ground. She did not move for a moment, but sat on lazily, still half asleep. Then, suddenly, it came to her that the voices were those of lovers. A man's voice low and teasing; a girl's, laughing and murmuring back. They must be sitting on the other side of the tree. She was eavesdropping and must move away at once, for they could not have seen her. Still, something about the girl's laugh sounded familiar. She was bending down to retrieve her book when she heard her say, *"Taisez-vous, Alfred!"* and caught a flutter of cherry-colored ribbon peeping round the bark.

She rose quickly and walked around the tree to the other side. She had to, to regain the path. Maria jumped up and so did a languid, foreign-looking man, glossily dressed. He bowed imperturbably, seeing that Maria was about to greet this sudden apparition.

"Why, Miss Brontë!" Maria looked discomposed for a moment, then, recovering her aplomb, "May I present my friend Count de Hamel? Count *Alfred* de Hamel!" Her eyes shone mischievously as she made the introduction.

For a moment Charlotte wondered what she should do or say. But just then more voices sounded, coming through the wood. The De Bassompierres and their party were bearing down on them. Evidently Count de Hamel belonged to it, too, and he and Maria had merely separated themselves from it for a little private dalliance.

Had it been dalliance? Charlotte told herself that she could not be sure. Neither her mind nor her ears had been properly awake when she first heard the voices. The De Bassompierre party stood around her, the women with their parasols closed now they had come into the shade. They acknowledged her curtsey with brief nods and hats raised a fraction of an inch. Then they swept the other two away with them again and left her standing there. She was only one of the teachers at Maria's *pensionnat.* A plain, insignificant-looking little thing.

She walked rapidly home, for now the afternoon was

quite spoiled. She hated the thought, that, like Madame Héger herself, she had spied on Maria. Inadvertently, but still—she felt sorrier than ever for the faithful John.

For the rest of the evening she tried to make up her mind what to do. It was useless to talk to Maria herself; to ask her any questions. Finally, for she knew Madame's coffee party must long have finished, she tapped on the door of her little parlor.

"May I speak to you, Madame?"

"But certainly." Madame was resting, with her small sandaled feet up on a footstool. She had opened the shutters now that the evening had come. A cool air stole through the room.

"I have been in the park. I met Maria with a Count Alfred de Hamel. Do you know him? I thought I should mention it in case you—disapproved."

Madame Héger crossed one tiny foot over the other. She gave Charlotte a sharp glance, belying the ease of her posture. "The De Bassompierres were there, too?"

Charlotte hesitated. "They joined them presently. He seemed to belong to their party."

"Then it is their responsibility, not mine. Thank you, Miss Charlotte."

Charlotte prepared to go. She wished she had said nothing after all. Yet the appearance of the Count, his low, confidential voice, had stuck in her throat. But she had salved her conscience now.

"Miss Charlotte?"

She turned again at the door.

"You asked if I knew the Count. I do. He is a frivolous waster. I have already forbidden him to call here. You must see that he does not visit Maria under my roof. For the rest, it is not my affair."

So all Madame Héger cared about was what happened under her roof. The reputation of the *pensionnat* must be preserved. Not, especially, Maria's.

"Thank you, Madame." Charlotte tried to keep the contempt and anger out of her voice, but only half succeeded. Madame Héger had the evening paper on her lap. She picked it up and began to read it.

CHAPTER *Fourteen*

Maria looked a little shy—or was it sly—when next they met, but Charlotte showed by her manner that she did not intend even to allude to Alfred. To lend an ear to confidences might be to encourage the silly flirtation, so she ignored the subject of their encounter in the park.

It was a week or two to the end of the holidays. Although she disliked most of the girls and found teaching them a great strain, she looked forward to that after all. It meant beginning her classes with Monsieur Héger again. She took her book into the garden one day. How delightful it was to have it to herself! The green arbor beckoned. She sat down at the end of the long tunnel of vines. The small grapes, half ripened, hung over her head. An insect buzzed, caught in the trap of greenery. But she and the insect were not long to have the tunnel to themselves.

Monsieur Héger appeared, carrying a ladder which he placed against the wall overhanging the arbor. He climbed up it and began clipping the vines. She saw his face looking at her through the leaves.

"Ah, Miss Charlotte! I interrupt your task?"

"Not at all. I'm only reading a novel."

"A *novel?*" His exclamation of wrath made her smile down at her book. She had provoked him on purpose. She meant to provoke him more.

"Why not, Monsieur? Everyone reads novels, you know."

"But you! You have no time to waste on trash! Did I not tell you to prepare a composition for me on the subject of Moses leading the Tribes through the Desert? Where is it, I ask? Where is it?"

She looked up at him through the leaves. "I don't think I'll write it. You told me not to exercise my imagination upon subjects on which I knew nothing. And I can't describe a desert because I've never seen one."

The brown eyes glared angrily down at her, then twinkled suddenly. "Ah, I see you are laughing at poor Constantin Héger who tries to keep your feet on the ground!"

"Laughing at you, Monsieur?"

"Now I don't laugh. I scold you instead. You have too heated a fancy. You will inflame it still further by occupying yourself with some nonsense written by a romantic woman for silly girls!"

"The book isn't written by a woman. It's written by a man."

"Give it to me."

She pretended not to hear him. A brown arm shot through the leaves menacingly. "Give it to me, I tell you! Give it at once!"

"Oh, certainly, if you want to read it yourself."

She thought she heard the ladder actually shake with his fury. "What do you mean to do with it then?" she asked as she handed it up.

"I will burn it! I will incinerate——"

"Burn a book like *Waverley?*"

"Ah!" There was a pause. She knew he was trying to read the title and author, to make sure she was not still teasing him. Then he sheepishly pushed it back at her through the leaves.

"You don't approve of Sir Walter Scott?"

"Forgive me, I might have known you would not waste your time on rubbish." She heard him give a great sigh. "It is deplorable that I cannot read English. A door, a great door, is forever closed to me."

"Monsieur, if you like I will teach you."

"You will? Ah, then we begin at the close of the holiday! Thank you, Miss Charlotte. Then, indeed, you may lecture me instead of my lecturing you."

It would be something to look forward to, next term. She wondered what sort of a pupil he would make. Would he burst with rage every time she corrected him? Or would his thirst for knowledge restrain him? It would be fun to see.

Clip-clip went the shears in silence for a little. Presently he said, "Your Queen comes tomorrow to visit our King. You have not forgotten it?"

"Monsieur, how can I! The Brussels newspapers have been full of the visit for weeks. I hear the streets are decorated already."

"You will try to see her, of course? My wife and I are invited to watch the procession from the window of a friend. It is a pity—I did suggest to my wife—but it appears that our friends have already invited a large party and so . . ."

So there is no room for me, Charlotte thought. Then her heart warmed to his evident sorrow. For it was obvious that he had tried to include her in the party and been rebuffed.

"I shall walk out to the Rue Royale," she said quickly, "with my short sight I shall see better, perhaps, from the pavement."

"Bien!" He sounded happy again. Then he became anxious once more. "You are so little, you must take care not to get crushed. But Mademoiselle Maria will be with you no doubt. She is English, too. She will protect you."

Charlotte left him with that impression. Well she knew that Maria was joining the De Bassompierres at *their* window. She was relieved, however, when Madame Héger's voice floated through the garden.

"Constantin? The supper is on the table."

The Hégers had their supper served first, in their own little parlor. Afterward, Jeanne, the elderly cook in sabots, would put hers and Maria's on a checked cloth spread at the end of the vast, deserted dining-room table. Monsieur scrambled down his ladder, which he left leaning against the garden wall. Charlotte picked up *Waverley* again. She had almost an hour to read, before going in to supper herself.

But with his disappearance the arbor felt cold and lonely. The sun had moved off and was sinking toward the west. Even the buzzing insects had gone. She got up and began to walk slowly through the garden, past the scented orange trees, past the roses bearing their second crop. The sky was turning a faint apricot pink. The bell of Saint Jacques rang out for the evening *salut.*

It was time to go indoors. She walked slowly up the long garden again, and past the mouth of the arbor. She saw Maria there, on the seat she had left.

"Are you coming for supper?" she called.

"I don't want any. I'm not hungry. I—I don't feel well."

Charlotte took a few steps down the tunnel and peered at her. She looked perfectly well, only a little tired. And no wonder, for she had had one late night after another, with rich suppers which had no doubt taken away her appetite.

"Oh, do go away!" Maria said crossly. "I only want to be left alone."

It was the first time Charlotte had ever known Maria to want to be left alone. Perhaps, she thought hopefully, she and Alfred have quarreled. Then patient John might get his chance after all.

She went into the dining room and ate her supper by herself. It was veal, deliciously cooked with mushrooms, and an equally delicious cold salad. Maria was fond of green salads as a rabbit. If only vexation ailed her, then some food would surely make her feel better. Charlotte took a tray from the sideboard, arranged a plateful of salad as temptingly as possible, buttered a roll, and went back with the tray to the garden again.

What was that murmuring sound from the arbor? Had the evening breeze sprung up already, stirring the leaves? She glanced at the heads of the flowers as she passed. No, they hung perfectly motionless. Her feet crunched on the gravel path. The murmuring stopped abruptly. There was some sort of a stir behind the arbor itself. A scrambling noise. And then a loud crash as the ladder placed under the wall fell to the ground.

She ran into the arbor and found Maria sitting alone. Maria jumped up when she saw her, exclaiming, "Oh, what was that noise?"

"The ladder falling from the side of the wall. Somebody must have knocked it down." She stared hard at Maria as she spoke. But Maria didn't even blush.

"How silly of me to get a fright! It was the wind of course."

"There is no wind," said Charlotte sternly. "Somebody climbed over the wall, kicked the ladder by mistake, and it fell down."

"Are you *sure* there's no wind? Because you know, it couldn't be anything else!"

"Look for yourself. Even the vine isn't stirring."

"Oh, well," said Maria, "it must have been some boy climbing over to steal the fruit. You know they do, sometimes."

"With you sitting there?"

Maria said rapidly, "I dare say that was what startled him. He would think the garden was empty. Then he would see me through the vines. He would scramble back again and kick the top of the ladder with his toe by mistake. Just as you said."

Charlotte couldn't answer that. She might be right after all. Boys did climb the wall after the fruit; Monsieur Héger was always making fierce sorties, hoping to catch them.

"I brought you out some supper," Charlotte said coldly.

"I don't think I want——" Maria glanced at the tray and changed her mind. "Oh, salad! I believe I *could* manage a little. Thank you, Miss Brontë, you are very kind. Will you just put the tray down beside me?"

"I did not realize it was getting quite cool and damp. You had better eat it indoors after all."

"But——"

"Come on, Maria."

Charlotte marched back toward the house. Maria followed her sulkily.

CHAPTER *Fifteen*

Her Majesty Queen Victoria of England was paying a state visit to her uncle, King Leopold of the Belgians. It was a holiday all over the country. Laden coaches drove in to Brussels letting down their loads of holidaymakers. Fisher-folk in their best clothes came from Ostend and the coast; farmers, their wives agog in new bonnets, their children clutched with each hand, came from inland; parties of school children arrived from Bruges and Ghent, in the charge of white-coiffed, perspiring nuns: all to watch the great procession and the fireworks and illuminations at night.

Madame Héger had spoken to Charlotte the evening before.

"After the procession, my husband and I intend to visit his mother out in the country. There is no diligence which can bring us back suitably until early next morning. Will you be good enough to see that the front door is locked at a reasonable hour?"

"Yes, Madame."

"Pierre should attend to it, of course, but he is apt to get drunk on fête days. Maria will be with the De Bassompierres all day, I believe. But I have sent a note to Madame de Bassompierre, saying she must be returned by ten o'clock."

"And if I should wish to see the illuminations myself?"

Madame gazed serenely back at Charlotte. "You must make sure that Maria has returned first. You must exercise *La Surveillance* with Maria during our absence. She requires it."

The streets were sure to be choked with traffic, so Monsieur and Madame Héger set off before seven o'clock next morning. They had to make their way on foot to the house of their friends. The De Bassompierre's carriage came an hour later to fetch Maria. Its powerful pair of horses, its massive bulk of upholstery, silver fittings and huge rubbered wheels, would insure a passage through the crowds.

After her own breakfast Charlotte went upstairs to put on her bonnet. Pierre and his wife had already gone. They would be gone all day. They had left a cold luncheon set out for her. Otherwise, nobody seemed to trouble whether she saw the Queen or not. She slipped out of the house, locking the door again carefully behind her and dropping the key into the pocket of her skirt. The quiet residential district around the Rue d'Isabelle seemed curiously empty this morning. Everyone must have left for the center of the town already, except herself.

She walked through the quiet streets, toward the rising hubbub from the Old Town. She entered the Rue Royale, where a kindly gendarme escorted her across the street already lined by mounted troops. He edged her safely onto the pavement, then left her there. She was so tiny, nobody bothered to push her out of the way; they could easily see over her head.

The distant blare of a band. The sudden stiffening of troops brought to attention. A low-slung carriage was bowling by with King Leopold of the Belgians, a handsome man in his fifties, seated on the far side from Charlotte, and a very small, very plump girl in her early twenties beside him.

"Vive la Reine d'Angleterre!" shouted the crowd.

Victoria turned her neat head to acknowledge the salute. For that second, her pale blue, protuberant eyes stared right down into Charlotte's wide hazel ones. Charlotte curtseyed as low as she could. When she rose again, the carriage had gone.

"Why, she's as small as I am!" was her first surprised thought as she tried to work her way out of the crowd again.

For a little while she wandered throughout the streets to look at the decorations. Flags bearing the British and the Belgian colors waved languidly above her head. The initial V. seemed all over the city; enameled with bedded-out flowers in the parks, or waving above the shops. She walked on through the heat, past the crowds like a small leaf blown along by them.

She could not bear to return to the empty house in the Rue d'Isabelle. The thought of eating a lonely cold supper there revolted her. And yet she had had no lunch. It was late enough for a drowsy stillness to have fallen over the city. The townspeople had gone back home for a meal and a rest before the festivities of the evening. The strangers were picnicking in the parks.

She went into a restaurant and ordered some rolls and fruit. The waiter stared at her, coming in alone, until he heard her accent and knew she was English. The English were all mad. They liked to walk proudly alone, yes, even their women. Or so he had heard.

She stayed, resting, until she felt other people were staring at her, too. Everyone else was in a gay party, nobody seemed to be alone but herself. She got up hastily, feeling they were laughing at her. She would be better behind the walls of the *pensionnat* after all.

She arrived there, footsore and tired. It was late now and quite dark. The servants must have returned after all, for she could smell the rank, cheap tobacco Pierre smoked. It would be an hour or more before Maria returned, too. Not so very much longer to be alone.

She went slowly upstairs and entered their room. There already, to her surprise, was Maria who seemed to stare at her with equal astonishment.

"I thought you would be at the Jenkins'," Maria exclaimed, "you—you always have supper with them on fête days."

"Have you forgotten they are still at Ostend?"

"Dieu! So I did."

Charlotte laid her bonnet and purse down on her bed. *"I* thought you were still with the De Bassompierres. It's not ten o'clock yet, you know."

When she came in, Maria seemed to be searching through her wardrobe. Now she yawned ostentatiously saying, "I'm quite worn out, you know. People ask me out so much! I felt too exhausted to continue the evening and decided to come home to bed."

Charlotte looked at her suspiciously. "How did you get in? I had the key; I did not expect you to return before ten."

"Pierre let me in by the back door. He's half tipsy already, but he and Jeanne mean to go out again, later, to see the illuminations. Why don't you go with them?"

"And Pierre half tipsy? No, thank you! If I go out again tonight, I shall go alone. There are sufficient crowds to make for safety."

"You should certainly go!" Maria said eagerly. "There can be no danger, with the streets all ablaze, and—oh, yes, the fireworks! Besides, nobody's likely to notice you anyway." She gave another great yawn and started undressing. "Don't wake me up when you come back, that's all I ask."

Charlotte went downstairs again. She decided to eat some supper after all. Only one small lamp had been lit in the dining room, but the dim light rested her nerves. She was no longer so footsore. A delicious coolness came through the window, laden with the scent of the orange blossoms in the garden. A little while ago she had felt herself far too tired to even think of going out again. Now she remembered that from the end of the street, one could see right down into the heart of the Old Town.

The illuminations there, at least, would be worth seeing. And she could watch them from just outside the *pensionnat*. She ate a mouthful or two, then went upstairs again and put on her bonnet once more. Maria seemed asleep already. There she lay, curled into a ball which made her look so deceptively smaller than she really was. Charlotte paused a moment, listening to her regular breathing. Then, very softly so as not to disturb her, she unfastened the door of her own little wardrobe, took out a shawl as protection from the night air, and let herself out of the house.

The soft summer darkness enfolded her. A slit of light from a side window on the *pensionnat* showed that Pierre and his wife were still indoors. Standing there, listening, Charlotte could hear the excited throb of the city reaching up to her. From somewhere came the steady thump-thump of a band. It was too far away for her to make out the tune, but the rhythm was intoxicating. And now, as she watched, the first of the night's fireworks sailed slowly, majestically into the sky: a golden star, pausing at the height of its arc to shatter itself into a shower of glittering fragments.

It must have been sent up from the park. Charlotte watched its rise and fall with a mounting thrill of excitement. So much beauty and magic tonight! It was like one of her own fantastic dreams. As one acts in a dream without thinking, she ran hastily down the street, out of it, and toward the center of the town and the park, where the star had fallen.

CHAPTER *Sixteen*

The park gates, usually closed at sundown, stood open tonight. The avenue was a moving mass of people. The roadway before the park gates was as bright as day. Along it streamed carriages, some gaily beribboned, to halt at the entrance, letting down their occupants to swell the crowd inside the park still further.

Over the open gates there glittered an arch of colored lights spelling out Victoria and Leopold. Charlotte passed under the lights and moved up the center avenue with the throng. The fountain with its stone basin at the end of the avenue was transformed, too, by the magic of the night. Now its waters shone green like emeralds, now they had changed to spouts of orange flames, now they were red like blood.

Some children had paused by the basin, holding out their little hands toward the water spouts above it, shouting with joy as hands and wrists became stained with color. Charlotte paused, too. She held out her own hands, small as any child's, and watched with the same delight as the light changed them to tiny green claws, or blue, or orange.

But when they turned blood-red, she pulled them hastily back to her side and walked on.

The band was in front of her now. The lights played on the bandsmen's new uniforms and caught the bandmaster's gold-tipped baton, making it glitter and wink. They were playing a selection of English airs as a compliment to the visiting Queen. Charlotte thought she recognized "Cherry Ripe," but she was not sure for its tempo was changed and the band obviously was not at home with such foreign tunes. She passed on, smiling to herself.

She was exquisitely happy. This enchantment made her forget everything but the moment. The whole park was changed. It was under the same spell as herself. Its *parterres* of flowers were invisible, but it glowed instead with flame-flowers sparkling and nodding from trees where, by everyday light, no flowers ever bloomed. There were planned spectacles of lighting, too. At the end of that path to the left, stood a giant ibis, shimmering in silver. Far ahead gleamed an obelisk with a crouching sphinx, fiery-eyed, at its feet. She stretched out her hands in pleasure and greeting toward them. She moved forward, unselfconscious, feeling herself invisible, one of the crowd.

And the happy crowd took her to itself. Here, in the heart of a foreign city, at nearly midnight, she was perfectly safe. The crowd itself protected her, with its good humor, its family parties, its equal pleasure in the magnificent sights around. Nobody had time even to glance sideways at the little figure drifting along alone. Yet she did not feel alone either. For this was the world that she, with her sisters and brother, had inhabited from childhood. The world of fantasy Monsieur Héger so often warned her against, because he said it did not exist.

Just then, it suddenly faded and came to an end. The last set piece of fireworks had died out of the sky. Gradually, the strange fruit and gems hanging from the trees vanished, leaving only blackness behind. The water in the Great Basin changed color for the last time, and now splashed invisibly into the dark rim of the surrounding stone.

The bandsmen were putting away their instruments. The paths, the broad avenue itself, were only illumined now by the usual gas lamps with long stretches of darkness between. The crowd turned and, slightly panicking, made for the gates before they could be closed against them. Charlotte was borne along by its pressure. She was leaving the Garden of Eden behind her. She darted across the pavement to get out of the way of the carriage wheels that would take the fashionables home. As she paused a moment to get her breath, she heard the great bell of Sainte Gudule ring out warningly over the city. Midnight! Time for Cinderella to return to her tasks.

Yet the magic still stayed with her as she climbed through the emptying streets to the Rue d'Isabelle once again. She was still bewitched. All her tiredness had flown. In her thoughts, she was still down below, in that magic garden of lights and fantasy. As she turned into the Rue d'Isabelle at last, she scarcely noticed a carriage bowling swiftly toward her. She would have forgotten its passage the next moment had not the flicker of a white handkerchief, waved through the window, caught her eye. Surely not waved at her! But the street was quite empty and silent, there was nobody in it except herself. Puzzled, but scarcely wakened out of her dream, Charlotte pushed the door of the *pensionnat* gently open, and heard it click behind her as she stepped into the darkened hall.

The moon shone through the staircase window, lighting her way upstairs. It shone through the dormitory window, which Maria had not bothered to curtain. There she lay, nestled down low in the bedclothes as usual, with only one bright curl showing against her pillow. Charlotte undressed quietly and hastily so as not to disturb her, and was herself asleep in a moment.

The day and the night had exhausted her more than she knew. She slept late and only woke when the sun began to stream down on her face. Because it was still the holidays there had been no harsh bell rung to rouse the boarders. Within reason, she and Maria might come down when they chose for their *petit dejeuner*. But within reason. She pulled Aunt Branwell's little enameled watch out from under her pillow. It was nearly ten o'clock!

"Wake up, Maria!"

But Maria never moved. She was always difficult to rouse in the mornings. Charlotte jumped out of bed, remembering that the Hégers expected to be back for breakfast; hating the thought that they would consider her a sluggard. She pulled on some clothes hastily, splashed her face and hands in the basin of cold water on the washstand, and then, in her petticoat went over to Maria's bed to shake her awake.

"Maria! It's nearly ten o'clock." But Maria did not stir. So Charlotte took hold of the long curl still visible above the sheet and gave it a gentle tug.

The next moment she screamed out loud. For the curl had come away in her hand. It had been cut neatly off from somewhere close to Maria's shining head. Its end was neatly tied with blue ribbon, and a scrap of paper was wound through the ribbon. Maria's handwriting stared up at her mockingly:

When this you see,
Remember me.
I shall be the Countess Alfred de Hamal then!

Charlotte fell on the bedclothes and shook them savagely. The bolster had been laid down the middle of the bed, the clothes molded about it to the shape of a human form. As she dropped the sheets back again, that flicker of a handkerchief returned to her memory. She knew now who had waved so mockingly from the carriage.

She brushed and smoothed her hair mechanically, thinking: I must tell Madame Héger at once. And what will she say? She picked up the dress she had worn yesterday, because it was handiest and lay on the chair where she had placed it in her weariness the night before, instead of hanging it up in the cupboard as she usually did. Then she walked downstairs with the note in her hand.

The Hégers had finished breakfast. Charlotte's interview with Madame Héger was not a pleasant one; but she was conscious of Monsieur Héger's sympathy and understanding, although he remained silent. After it was over, she stole out into the garden to try to refresh her spirits.

The path wound under the window of the little parlor she had just left. She glanced through it as she hurried by. Monsieur Héger had apparently left the room. Madame had laid her sewing aside and had seated herself at her escritoire. She was busy writing a letter.

The arbor looked green and cool. Charlotte went toward it, and then, deflecting her steps, avoided it after all. The memory of that overturned ladder kept her from going there. No doubt Alfred had used the ladder to climb over the wall and make his final arrangements with Maria for their elopement. And Maria must have been expecting him that evening when she so obstinately refused to come in and have supper.

Charlotte wondered, miserably, what difference it might have made if she had come out to the arbor just a few seconds earlier and caught them together. But what did it matter now? The day passed slowly enough. She was invited to eat her meals with Monsieur and Madame, since it was ridiculous for her to be seated alone in the great dining room now that Maria was gone. Her name was not mentioned. Madame Héger seemed determined to ignore the whole unfortunate occurrence. But Charlotte felt uncomfortably certain that she was being blamed in part for it.

The new term started. She found herself looking forward eagerly to her lessons with Monsieur Héger. She looked on him now as her only friend. The hours she spent studying with him were increasingly stimulating and happy.

It was toward the end of the term that Madame summoned her to the parlor. She spoke kindly enough.

"Miss Charlotte, I have been occupying myself with your plans, your aspirations to keep a school. You are now well equipped for the project. Your sisters will wonder, perhaps, what keeps you so long abroad?"

Charlotte felt vaguely surprised. "My sisters understand quite well that you require my help next term also. And after your, and Monsieur's, kindness to me——"

Madame made a little gesture. "Think nothing of that, Mademoiselle. It is of your own future that you should think. I heard from Mr. Wilson yesterday. He is willing to come back. He will undertake your duties next term. You are at liberty to leave."

Charlotte stood speechless. After a moment she managed to ask, "When would you like me to leave?"

"I would not *like* you to leave." The other said with smooth courtesy, adding in the same cold tones. "Your work has been admirable. But you came in the first place, to learn French, *hein?* You have succeeded sufficiently to add our language to your curriculum."

Charlotte only repeated steadily, "When would you like me to leave?"

Madame shrugged her plump shoulders. "When you please. You are welcome to remain here as our guest until the new term begins."

"Oh, no, Madame. If I am of no further use to you, I shall not burden your hospitality. I should like to go tomorrow."

"As you wish."

The coach for Ostend left next morning at ten. Pierre carried down her box and received her parting tip with his usual surliness. A cab was at the door. Madame Héger came into the hall as she moved toward it. She placed a little bouquet of flowers in Charlotte's hands.

"Good-by, Mademoiselle. My very good wishes for the success of your school. It will be admirably run, I am sure. Be so kind as to inform us when it is opened. It is more than possible that we shall place Louise, our eldest girl, in your care."

Charlotte recognized that it was Madame's way of indicating that she wished to make amends. But she could not bring herself to acknowledge either this, or the bouquet, by more than a cold bow and a murmur of thanks. Monsieur held the door open for her. But he did not step back into the house again. Instead, he entered the cab and seated himself beside her.

"You are coming with me?"

"I cannot allow you to start your journey alone."

He saw her into the coach and stood there, at the window, looking white and miserable. "We both know your integrity, Miss Charlotte. And I know more. I have taught you now, for a long while. I have tried to open a mind already open and superior to any other mind I have cultivated. If sometimes, in my zeal, I have been angry, forgive me."

"Monsieur, there is nothing to forgive. I have learned more from you than from anyone else in the world."

He brightened; looked a little happier. Now he was pulling a book out of his pocket. He dropped it gently onto her lap. It was a volume of Lamartine's poems.

"Take this as a parting souvenir. When you read it, remember Constantin Héger."

"Monsieur, I shall never forget you. I don't need the book for that!"

There was perfect understanding between them as they looked at each other for the last time. But as the wheels began to turn, taking her away from him, Charlotte knew she would never part with the book.

PART THREE 1844–1848

Charlotte and Fame

CHAPTER *Seventeen*

A neat package, fresh from the printers at Keighley, lay on the parlor table of the parsonage. Charlotte, now home again, opened it while her sisters looked eagerly over her shoulder.

"Yes, the printer has done exactly what we required," she said.

The package contained a pile of prospectuses for the new school. Each was headed THE MISSES BRONTËS' ESTABLISHMENT FOR THE BOARD AND EDUCATION OF A LIMITED NUMBER OF YOUNG LADIES. THE PARSONAGE. HAWORTH.

Anne snatched up one and danced round the room, reading it aloud. The Terms (it said) were to be £35 per annum for Board and Education. French, German, Latin, Music, Drawing, Use of the Pianoforte and Washing were extras. Each young lady was to be provided with one pair of sheets, pillow cases, four towels, a dessert spoon, and a teaspoon. A quarter's notice or a quarter's board was required previous to the removal of a pupil.

Anne's voice faltered at the mention of the thirty-five pounds. "Are you sure that isn't too much?"

"No," said Charlotte firmly. "Superior establishments

always charge that. Now please, Anne, be quiet while I write to Ellen and send her some prospectuses to distribute. She said she would. I think half a dozen would be enough, don't you? If she wants more she can easily have them."

So presently, away in another part of Yorkshire, Ellen ordered the carriage and called on all her parents' friends who had daughters of the right age. Some of them asked bluntly, "But where *is* Haworth, my dear?" Others, who knew already of its isolation amid the moors, looked thoughtful, or said right away, "But there will be no advantages—no concerts or society in such a place!" And when Ellen had gone, they tore the little prospectus up and dropped the pieces in the wastepaper basket.

For the rest of that summer, the Brontë girls tried to find pupils, but no pupils would come. They were glad now, that they had not spent precious money in building an extension to the parsonage as they had once, wildly, thought of doing. It would only have been wasted.

When the first sharp tang of autumn arrived, Anne went back to the Robinsons while Charlotte sat down to write to Ellen again, sad but reconciled at last to the failure of their great plan.

"I fear you are giving yourself too much trouble on our account," she wrote. "Depend upon it, if you were to persuade a mamma to bring her child to Haworth the aspect of the place would frighten her, and she would probably take the dear girl back instanter. We are glad we have made the attempt, and we will not be cast down because it has not succeeded."

It was the year 1844. Tabby had grown old and easily fussed, so Martha now did most of the work. Mr. Brontë's eyes began to trouble him seriously and Charlotte had to spend much time reading aloud to him. Perhaps it was as well that the school project had failed. She told herself this after she had gathered the few remaining prospectuses together and burned them at the back of the kitchen fire.

Emily's arm had now a deep scar on it. One day, when it was breathlessly hot and still, she had stood at the gate of the parsonage, looking down the steep cobbled lane. She saw a strange dog running straight from the moor, its head down, foam at its mouth. Poor thing, thought Emily, it must be frantic with thirst! Quickly she ran back to the house, got a bowl of water and was back on the road again as the dog ran toward her. She had never feared an animal in her life, nor had any animal feared her. She stepped right in its path, meaning to stop it and put down the bowl. It sprang at her, red-eyed. Its fangs pierced the skin of her arm, drawing blood. Then it ran on, blindly, its head to the ground. Emily knew now, it was mad.

She looked at the wound on her arm. It must be cauterized directly. There was no doctor at hand. She went back into the parsonage, glad that no one was about to make any fuss. Tabby was spending the afternoon with her sister. Martha was out at the back. Without giving herself time to shrink, she walked into the kitchen, heated an iron red-hot in the fire, and pressed it hard to the wound.

The pain made her feel sick, and so did the smell of burning flesh. But she held the hot iron without flinching, until she was sure that the risk of catching hydrophobia from the mad dog's bite was over. Presently she got up, shakily, and searched for a clean cloth to make a bandage. When Charlotte and Anne came in from the moor, they saw her with her arm in a sling.

"It had to be done at once," was all she would say.

Time went on. Their father had a new curate now, a tall Irishman called Arthur Bell Nicholls. He was very different from poor Celia Amelia. Good-looking enough, but taciturn and terribly shy. But Mr. Brontë could put up with him, and that was all that mattered.

The doctor had diagnosed cataract as being the trouble with Mr. Brontë's eyes. He said it must be allowed to run its course, which might even take a year or two. Then, when the gray film had grown to cover the eyes, an operation could be thought of. If it was successful, he would regain his sight. But meanwhile . . .

Mr. Nicholls had to read the Lessons now in church, and sometimes preach the sermon, too. Mr. Brontë spoke little of the dreadful prospect. He remained calm and cheerful, though still preferring the solitude of his study, and avoiding, if possible, any call upon his daughters to help him. When sitting reading or writing at the table in the parlor, Charlotte's ears were always strained now to hear the uncertain step, the stumble in mounting the stairs. Then she or one of the others would jump up and appear at his elbow as if by accident, for the proud old man hated to ask for assistance.

Anne was now at home as well as the other two, and one day the idea had taken Mr. Brontë to walk to Keighley. Emily had been hurriedly summoned to go with him. Anne had chosen to go, too. Charlotte, left behind, sat sewing until it was time to set the supper table. Emily's writing things were strewn over one end of it. As she picked up a notebook to tidy it away, it opened of itself in her hand.

She found herself reading a poem—Emily's poem because it was in Emily's handwriting and echoed pictures in Emily's mind:

Silent is the House—all are laid asleep;
One, alone, looks out o'er the snow wreaths deep,
Watching every cloud, dreading every breeze
That whirls the wildering drifts, and bends the groaning
trees.

Burn, then, little lamp; glimmer straight and clear.
Hush! a rustling wing stirs, methinks, the air:
He for whom I wait, thus ever come to me;
Strange Power! I trust thy might; trust thou my constancy.

What did Emily mean? She went on reading. The "strange power" was there. Each poem was different but it was there, in them all. Yes, even in the gentler ones, like this one to the moon:

> *How clear she shines! How quietly*
> *I lie beneath her guardian light;*
> *While heaven and earth are whispering me,*
> *"Tomorrow, wake, but dream tonight . . ."*

Yes, that was Emily, too. Charlotte read on, fascinated. Her study of good poetry under Monsieur Héger let her recognize it when she saw it. And the more she read, the more she became determined that the world, too, must read these poems of her sister's.

They must be published.

She was so absorbed in the notebook, she never heard the steps of the returning walkers come over the gravel path outside. She was unconscious that Emily, nearest the window, had looked in and seen her. Next moment a whirlwind had rushed into the room and snatched the notebook out of her hand.

"How dare you, Charlotte!"

"Forgive me, Emily, I didn't mean to pry. I just lifted the notebook in order to set the supper table and it opened——"

"And you read! You *did* pry!"

"Girls, girls, what is this?" Mr. Brontë stood in the doorway. Anne's frightened face showed beside him. "Calm yourself, Emily. Of what do you accuse Charlotte?"

"Of meddling with my private papers. Of reading what was never intended for any eyes but my own!"

Charlotte lost her own temper at this point. "How could I know that the notebook was private? It did not say so on the cover. Emily is making a ridiculous fuss about nothing, Papa!"

Mr. Brontë's face was stern as it turned toward the quarreling sisters. "You have both forgotten yourselves. Let me hear no more of such nonsense!" He turned his back on them and walking into his study, shut the door upon this unusual disturbance.

By suppertime Charlotte began to feel she had been, indeed, in the wrong. Yet Emily was unreasonable not to have understood how it happened! She murmured an apology as they sat down to table. Emily received it in silence. The whole meal was also eaten in silence, for Anne, frightened and not quite knowing what had happened, made a few trembling remarks and then sat quiet, too.

Anne had to wait for an explanation until they went upstairs to bed. Charlotte was brushing her beautiful silky hair—the only beauty she had besides her eyes—at the mirror. A candle flickered on the dressing table beside her.

"Charlotte—what happened?"

"I opened a book of Emily's by mistake. I didn't mean to pry, Anne!"

"Of course not. But why was she so angry?"

"Because it contained her poems, her most private thoughts. Yet what else is real poetry—great poetry—made out of?"

"You mean her poems were—great?"

Charlotte nodded. The candle flame reflected her eyes in the glass, making them look enormous. "They *must* be published. They are far, far better than anything I ever managed to do myself."

Anne said slowly, "If Emily was so upset at you, her own sister, reading them, she isn't likely to let the world read them."

"No. That's what I'm afraid of. But I'll wait until she has calmed down. Then I'll do my best to persuade her."

Emily was still cold and distant next day. She took herself on to the moor with Keeper and nobody saw her until the evening. By then she seemed to have walked herself into a calmer, more reasonable frame of mind. At supper that night she turned to Charlotte and said, "I remembered to get you that Life of Pitt from the library yesterday. You did say you wanted to read it, didn't you?"

"Yes, I did. Thank you."

Charlotte took care to speak casually, as Emily had spoken. But she knew the episode was to be forgiven and forgotten, and that Emily, too, was ashamed now of the fuss she had made.

How much more fuss would she make when the subject of printing her poems was broached? Charlotte didn't dare to mention the subject until a day or two more had passed, and they had completely returned to their old relationship. She waited, too, until Anne was present to back her up, if possible.

All three girls were cleaning Aunt Branwell's room, now the spare bedroom of the parsonage. Emily had brought the stepladder upstairs and, climbing it, had dusted out the ceiling cornices. Anne had swept the floor. Charlotte had washed the paintwork. Now Anne had subsided on Aunt Branwell's sofa, too tired to do anything more for the present. Emily was eying the pictures, deciding whether their gold frames needed rubbing up or not.

Charlotte, her back turned to the other two, was dusting the mantelpiece. She was glad that her face was hidden from Emily as she spoke.

"Emily—I want you to publish your poems."

Emily lifted a picture down from the wall before she even bothered to reply. "Do you? I don't."

"But they're so wonderful! So true and full of feeling. A thousand times better than mine. Emily, please——"

"I don't want to discuss it any further."

Charlotte knew she was beaten, for the time being. But next day she returned to the charge.

"Emily, I meant what I said. Anne and I would be prepared to subscribe to a printing, if necessary. But, you know, what we always wished for was—fame. Branwell with his painting, you, Anne, and I with our writing. If you're the one who attains it, we shall be happy for your sake. At least one of us will have made a name outside Haworth!"

They were picking the currants from the bushes at the bottom of the garden. Each held a white china pudding bowl into which she dropped the fruit. Emily looked through the straggling bushes at her little, grave sister. She was touched.

"If one of us deserves fame then all do," she said in a softened voice. Then, more briskly, "But what have we done to expect it? We have scribbled away all our lives for our own pleasure. It would be best not to talk of fame."

"Still, one can't help thinking about it, can one? Though perhaps 'recognition' is a better word than fame."

Emily's bowl was now full of fruit. She exchanged it for Anne's half-empty one and continued to travel along the canes. Presently she said in a muffled sort of voice, "Besides, there aren't enough poems to make a book worth printing."

Charlotte's heart leaped with joy at the words. They meant that Emily was seriously considering her suggestion. Neither of them noticed Anne steal away with the bowlful of currants toward the house. But when she came back to them, she was carrying a little notebook instead.

"I know my poetry won't be as fine as Emily's," she said shyly, "but if I've written anything worth adding to hers, to make up a book . . ."

Charlotte took the poems and read them aloud. Anne stood there trembling, awaiting her sisters' judgment. The songs she had written were sweet and true. They lacked the soaring strength of Emily's, but they had their own music. When Charlotte's voice ceased at last, Emily nodded her head.

"If you risk it, so shall I," she said.

CHAPTER *Eighteen*

"Gentlemen,

May I request to be informed whether you would undertake the publication of a collection of short poems in one volume, 8vo. If you object to publishing the work at your own risk, would you undertake it on the author's account?

I am, gentlemen,
Your obedient humble servant,
C. BRONTË."

Charlotte read her letter aloud for her sisters' approval. Then she addressed it to the firm of publishers which, after much trouble and thought, they had chosen. Messrs. Aylott and Jones, Paternoster Row, London. Now it lay on the parlor table, ready to be collected by Mr. Feathers when next he arrived with the post.

Only Emily, remembering the signature, made an objection. "I thought we had decided not to use our own names?"

"Of course not. But if I used a fictitious name, we might never receive the reply. I've thought it all out. I shall act as agent for the three of us. Then they need never know——"

"That your own poems are in the book as well?" Anne put in with a gentle smile.

It had been Anne and Emily's turn to persuade Charlotte to include some of her own work. She had plenty to choose from. Like the others, she had always enjoyed scribbling down verses. But she knew that Emily's were much the best.

The manuscript was ready, all except the signatures. For days they had been debating what names they should choose. It was Charlotte again who suggested wasting no more time. They could think that problem out while awaiting the answer to the letter. They must choose names that would give no hint as to whether they were men or women. That would be the safest way to ensure against discovery. Women's work was but lightly thought of then. Many professional women writers had tried to evade the prejudice against their sex by boldly choosing a man's name as a pseudonym. But the sisters' scruples would not allow them to do that. No. They must choose names less decidedly masculine, so that at any rate there could be no real deception about their sex.

And they would stick to their own first initials. So Emily had chosen Ellis; Anne, Acton; and Charlotte (remembering the first name of a Yorkshire bibliophile) would call herself Currer, except when using her real name to transact the business end of the matter.

But the surname?

"Something beginning with a B," said Emily firmly.

They sat round the table ringing the changes on B. Beresford, Ballantine, Bartholemew. Nothing seemed quite right.

"They're all too long," Charlotte said. "We want something simple and short like Brown. Oh, but I didn't mean Brown exactly. Everyone chooses a name like Brown when they want to hide under a false one."

A shadow fell between themselves and the sun. It was Mr. Arthur Bell Nicholls, their father's new curate, passing the window. Anne looked up suddenly and suggested, "What about Bell?"

Bell was just right. Ellis, Acton, and Currer Bell. Each in her tiny meticulous handwriting the girls added "Bell" to the names they had chosen. Then the little manuscript book was made up for the post, the accompanying letter slipped in, and the whole despatched.

Messrs. Aylott and Jones replied a few days later. They said they would be glad to publish the volume if its authors paid for the printing. They could not undertake this at their own cost because of the risk of producing work by unknown poets. After a little debate, the girls agreed to pay the sum asked.

It was dreadfully difficult to pass the time while waiting for their poems to be published. Charlotte and Anne busied themselves cleaning the house. Emily took Keeper for hours and hours out on the moor. She would walk till the sun began to set; till the mists fell like a curtain on the great hills in the distance. And when the mists were pierced by the last rays of light she would sometimes catch a momentary glimpse of the mysterious ridge in the distance, floating, gray as a cloud.

One evening she came home, sat down with a fresh, empty notebook and began to write. She wrote steadily, scarcely raising her head from each page. It was Charlotte who at last dared to ask, "What are you writing, Emily?"

Emily paused. Then she said slowly, "I am writing

the story of the great house on Withens Height, and the man who lived there."

"But there isn't any great house."

"Don't be so slow, Charlotte!" Emily spoke impatiently. "I'm making one out of the mist. An old, crumbling place with an inscription over the doorway. With vast rooms and rambling passages and stables behind. The thunderstorms catch it and the wind sweeps round it."

Charlotte was silent. She was seeing the house, too. Then— "Ellen spoke of such a house once. Did you or she not call it Wuthering Heights?"

"That's what I'm calling it now. That is the name of the book."

Emily picked up her pen and went on. Having created the house, she was now creating Heathcliff, the wild half-gypsy boy brought home one night by the master of Wuthering Heights; creating Catherine, the master's young daughter, who was Heathcliff's playmate until, when they were grown-up, they quarreled, and Catherine married somebody else, and Heathcliff took his dreadful revenge.

Those evenings after supper, the wind wuthered around the parsonage, too. Watching Emily absorbed, both Anne and Charlotte found the old desire to write awakening in them once more. Not poetry this time but prose.

Pictures of Brussels, its crowded streets, the quiet garden behind the *pensionnat* had often appeared to Charlotte as she lay awake in bed, listening to the wind; pictures of Monsieur and Madame Héger and Maria Miller, and the clashing of bells over the city. Yes, she would write a novel, and place most of it in Brussels. She would remember Monsieur Héger's advice and keep her feet on the ground. She would control her imagination and make her book a cool, clear picture of what she knew. She would write it in the first person. But then, would that not make it too personal? Not, perhaps, if she wrote as a man. Then it would seem, to any readers who knew her, more like fiction.

What would her hero be called? She thought of a mansion she had once seen called Crimsworth Hall. He would be called William Crimsworth. The tale would begin here, in Yorkshire. Crimsworth would start as a clerk in his elder brother's mill. She knew well the Yorkshire mills. Keighley was full of them, their owners and employees. Then Crimsworth would quarrel with his brother, seek his fortune abroad, and get taken on as Professor of English in a Brussels *pensionnat* very like the Pensionnat Héger.

She would call her book *The Professor.*

As she wrote, a love story crept into the book. There was a girl, a pupil, who learned English from William Crimsworth. The girl was poor even as she had been. She earned enough to pay for her lessons by making the delicate, fragile lace for which Brussels is famous. But she was no cipher of a girl. She had Charlotte's own independence, her own habit of arguing with her professor, her own great loneliness which was finally wiped away by her marriage to William Crimsworth. In fact, she was a prettier, somewhat gentler, version of Charlotte herself.

Of the three girls busily scribbling it was Anne who most closely obeyed Monsieur Héger's behest. Anne knew what she was going to write about from the first. "Nobody has written down exactly what it is like to be a governess," she said quietly. "So I am going to do so. It will be a plain, dull tale perhaps. But at least it will be a truthful one."

She called her heroine Agnes Grey. A plain, dull name, but she chose it on purpose. She wrote it down in the first person, too. "My father," she began, "was a clergyman in the north of England, who was deservedly respected by all who knew him . . ."

Agnes Grey endured all the slights, the servants' impertinences, the discomforts which governesses were often subjected to in these days, and which Anne and her sisters knew only too well. She lived in the midst of great wealth, without enjoying its benefits herself. She saw her eldest pupil make a marriage of convenience with no love on either side; and saw, too, the misery which followed. She tried to manage the younger ones who were quite undisciplined, thoughtless, and cruel to animals.

The only gleam in her existence came from her growing friendship with the young curate Weston, who was so kind to the sick and poor. As the book progressed, he grew more and more like the dead William Weightman.

They had gone back to their old habit of reading bits aloud and consulting one another. Just the three girls alone. The place where Branwell had sat sprawling and laughing, was empty now. He had taken odd jobs here and there because the world did not seem to value him as it should. He, the only gay, social member of the family, had even been reduced to serving as the booking clerk at a small railway halt. Now, because literature did not welcome him with open arms, he would turn his back on it; let it alone.

For the three girls, however, the cold bleak months before spring were entirely happy ones. During the daytime they performed their household tasks as thoroughly as they had always done. They saw that a good hot midday dinner was taken in to their father's study; that a place was set for Mr. Nicholls, the curate, if he required a meal. They were so absorbed in their inner lives of imagination they never noticed how Mr. Nicholls sometimes angled wistfully for an invitation to remain after the meal was over. How often his eyes rested on Charlotte particularly, before he picked up his hat, said good-by and walked slowly away to his lonely lodgings. Charlotte was glad that her father liked him. That was all.

The three sisters lived for the time after supper when Martha had cleared the dishes away and the notebooks could be brought out again. The strong wooden shutters were closed against the wuthering winds outside. The fire was poked into a blaze. Then each sister stepped back into the world she was busy creating. Charlotte as William Crimsworth once more trod the cobbles of the Rue d'Isabelle. Anne relived the humiliations of her old life as governess. And Emily? As the shutters rattled she seemed to hear the ghost of Catherine Linton crying outside, "Let me in—let me in!"

Presently the fire would die down and Mr. Brontë's step could be heard going up to bed; pausing to wind the tall clock halfway upstairs. And the sisters, returning to the parsonage with a jerk would put away their books regretfully so as to get enough sleep for tomorrow.

Now the days were growing a little longer. Spring would be here soon. The straggling bushes at the bottom of the garden began to put out green hints of what might be coming. The wind died down. One day during their midday dinner, Charlotte, looking out of the window and seeing a blue sky instead of a gray, said, "I believe the primroses will be out. I shall go down by the beck and look for some."

Mr. Nicholls said rather unwillingly, "I am sorry, Miss Charlotte. But the Thwaites children are ill and clamoring for you to finish the story you began last time you visited them. Still, I dare say tomorrow would do."

Charlotte's conscience told her tomorrow would not do. A day more is a long, long time for sick children to wait. However, she merely said, "Thank you for telling me, Mr. Nicholls," and when they had finished the meal, he saw her take the road down to the village instead of to the valley of the beck.

At supper that night, a bunch of primroses lay on her plate. She knew who had gathered them for her and was touched and surprised. To think that anyone so grim, so silent, would have made such a delicate gesture! She would thank him tomorrow when he came to the parsonage on his usual visit to Mr. Brontë to discuss parish affairs and the work to be done. Anne and Emily had not been out that day. It *could* have been nobody else but him.

Then she forgot him again in the pleasure of getting back to her book. She was no longer seated at the parsonage table. The yellow lamplight was sunshine, and the sunshine glittered through the leaves of the arbor in the *pensionnat* garden, and she was sitting in it—only not she, but William Crimsworth—watching Madame Héger—but she was called Mademoiselle Zoraide Reuter now—watering the flowers.

Soon the three novels were almost finished. Meanwhile, interrupting them, had come the proofs of the book of poems. The interruption was a delightful one. The poems looked what Anne called "real" now they were set up in print. They had to check them over carefully for printers' mistakes. One upset Charlotte very much. She had written "trembling stars" and the idiot of a man had set it up as "tumbling stars" which of course (as she wrote rather sharply to Messrs. Aylott and Jones) made the whole poem absurd.

However, such things would be put right in the final printing, but a good deal of correspondence had to pass back and forth, about where review copies were to be sent, and so on. It was Anne who suggested that Charlotte should enquire, at the same time, whether the firm would be interested in their novels.

"Agnes Grey is nearly finished," she said. "Perhaps one ought to ask now, where our books should be sent."

"We can't afford to pay again for printing," Charlotte said decidedly. "Besides, a novel is a different matter from poetry. More people buy novels, so why shouldn't they buy ours?"

Emily nodded agreement, so Charlotte wrote another letter. "Gentlemen," she wrote, "C., E. and A. Bell are now preparing for the press a work of fiction, consisting of three separate and distinct tales. . . . It is not their intention to publish these tales on their own account. They direct me to ask you whether you would be disposed to undertake the work. . . ."

And Messrs. Aylott and Jones replied, saying that unless they were paid, they would not.

"Never mind," said Anne when the somewhat damping letter arrived. "There are other printers and publishers in the world. If our poems sell well, and our names become known, I dare say in the end there will be no difficulty in getting our novels printed."

CHAPTER *Nineteen*

Of their first, previous book, sent out into the world with such trembling hope, only two copies were ever sold.

Messrs. Aylott and Jones had been right. Nobody much wanted to read poetry, unless it was signed by a famous name like Wordsworth or Southey. One copy was bought by a Mr. Enoch of Warwick. The girls knew that, because he liked the poems sufficiently to send his copy to the parsonage to be signed by the authors. At least they had been asked for their autographs! It was something.

Nobody knows who bought the other. If it should ever turn up, it would now be worth more than its weight in gold.

They had paid for some modest advertising. And they had sent copies to the chief magazines in hopes of reviews. There were one or two notices, but not many. The reviews, at least, were kind. The notice in *The Critic* even used the word "genius." But that did not help to sell the book.

They had spent about £46 on a failure, which in those days was worth about £200 or $600.00. It was a very big sum for the Brontë girls to lose. But they refused to be discouraged.

The three novels were finished at last. They sent them through the post to every likely firm.

They had something else to distract their attention as spring deepened into summer. Mr. Brontë's eyes were now pronounced ripe for operation. The famous oculist they had consulted, wanted it done in Manchester, where he lived. So, in between parceling up *The Professor* and sending it on its rounds, Charlotte made preparations for taking her father there.

The operation had to be done without anesthetics. It would be a terrible ordeal. He would either return home with his full sight restored, or be blind for the rest of his life. Nobody spoke about the latter possibility. Mr. Brontë faced it calmly, with the courage of all his family. Arthur Bell Nicholls would be in charge of the parish until he came back.

The Haworth gig was ordered to take them to Keighley station and Mr. Nicholls carried their small luggage out to it. He looked at Charlotte's pale face. His own was as pale. She wondered dimly why he should feel it as much as they did. She did not know, then, that he was feeling it for *her*.

But she was startled when this silent, apparently unemotional man, suddenly took one of her hands in both of his. "Anything I can do— You may rely upon me— I shall pray for you, Miss Charlotte. I shall pray for you earnestly."

Her large eyes were raised to him in surprise. "Pray for Papa," she said.

"Of course. Of course. I shall do that, too. But I want you to know that whatever the outcome, I shall remain here if I'm wanted. To help you all in any way that I can."

I shall remain here! That meant that, even if her father were completely blind, Mr. Nicholls would not desert him. He would not leave for another charge. A great feeling of gratitude welled up in Charlotte's heart. For the first time she thought of Arthur Nicholls as a man, and a man with as strong feelings as their own.

"I thank you," she murmured the words so low, he could scarcely hear them. But the look she gave him as she stepped into the gig showed that she could never treat him with the old indifference again.

They had taken furnished rooms in Manchester. The operation was to be done in Mr. Brontë's bedroom there. The day came. Charlotte woke in her bedroom next his, and wondered for a moment what it was that lay so heavily on her. Then she remembered. This was the day that would either bring full sight back to her father or take away the small glimmer still left to him.

She rose, dressed herself neatly as usual, and went in to see if he was comfortable and had had his breakfast. Then she entered the little parlor to have hers. The first thing she saw on the breakfast table was a package lying beside her plate. She knew from its shape what it was. It was done up in the very same piece of brown paper in which she had wrapped it for yet another journey. It was the returned manuscript of *The Professor.*

Listlessly she tore it. The usual letter fell out, saying the usual things, but so curtly, they pierced her steadiness at last. The publishers thanked Mr. Currer Bell for offering his novel, but were unable to use it. It was too short.

She was in no state of mind to bear this recurring blow. Now, for the first time, despair swept over her. Despair and a sort of unreasoning anger. Could they not have sent back the book on any other day but this? She laid her head down on the table and wept.

Presently she sat up again, dried her eyes and composed herself. The oculist would be here soon. This was no time to think of one's own disappointments. She went back to her father's room and saw that everything was ready. The table for the instruments, the water and towels and bandages. She tried to talk cheerfully, hopefully, to him as she moved about.

A ring at the doorbell. Heavy steps on the stairs. She saw her father stiffen and knew he was bracing himself for the ordeal. The oculist entered, with two other doctors. They asked if she wished to remain in the room. She nodded and said quietly that she did.

She held her father's hand all the while. The cataracts had to be cut out from the naked eyeball. He bore it without flinching and so did she. One of the doctors held his head firmly, since the slightest movement would make the knife slip. But he lay perfectly still, without moving.

The operation lasted a quarter of an hour. To Charlotte it seemed a lifetime. The room was heavily darkened now. Her father must lie still, without stirring for four days. They told her she must speak to him as little as possible so that he might not be tempted to answer and move the muscles of his face. The oculist said he was satisfied, but it all depended upon the next four days.

"I understand," Charlotte told him. "We will both obey your orders exactly."

"I shall come back and see how things go. But you must be prepared to remain here at least a month."

At first the length of time didn't seem to matter. But when the four days were over, when it was seen that Mr. Brontë's sight would indeed recover, both of them began to weary and fret to be home. He had still to lie in a darkened room, however, and though he urged, and even begged Charlotte to go out and get some air, she felt no inclination to do so.

The air of Manchester was smoky and stifling in this summer's heat. She knew nobody there. The endless rows of houses and shops, built of red brick and darkened by the fumes from the factory chimneys, repelled her. Oh for one breath of the scented air off Haworth Moor!

After her father had been settled down for the night, she scarcely knew what to do with herself. The long, weary evenings dragged on interminably. She had no heart to send *The Professor* anywhere else, not for the present, anyway. Besides, all the publishers had said the same thing. It was too short.

A thought came into her mind. She played with it, idly, and then with gathering enthusiasm. Supposing she were to begin something new? Something long enough to satisfy them. No, something to satisfy herself. She would not think of money or fame this time. She would build up another world of imagination, as she and her sisters had done long ago. Simply to occupy and amuse herself during the weeks of waiting.

She went out and bought a good thick notebook at a nearby stationers. That evening she sat down before it to decide what her heroine would be like. For it was to be a heroine this time. She was not going to hide under the mask of a William Crimsworth any longer. But the girl in the story must have some affinity with herself, or she could not write about her as if she were real. So she must be poor, like herself. Plain and small like herself. She had better be called Jane.

Jane what? Charlotte tried over one surname after the other. Then a name came suddenly to her, one she had seen carved on a tombstone years ago. It was a great stone and marble tomb in the church at Hathersage, a small Derbyshire village she had once visited with Ellen. The brass plate on the top had read: "Here lies Robert Eyre, Knight."

The girl would be called Jane Eyre.

She began the story that night. The story of the plain, passionate little orphan, tolerated in the house of her rich aunt and cousins. She saw again the great house, Stonegappe, where she herself had once been a governess and where Ellen had visited her that bright summer's day. That would be Jane's home. She saw, too, the Red Room where Ellen had laid off her bonnet. The room so seldom used, it would strike terror to the heart of a child with its cold mirrors and shrouded furniture. That was the room Jane would be locked into when she was naughty.

She saw Jane (but it was herself, now) sent to a boarding school as she had been. Felt the girls' teasing again, tasted the burnt porridge, endured the loneliness of having no one she wanted to be friendly with, or who wanted to be friendly with her, on account of her shabby clothes and her silence.

Jane grew up. She did some teaching at her old school.

Enough to justify her desperate move to get away from it by advertising for a post as governess somewhere else. She set off for the post she had found. It was to take charge of a little girl, the ward of a gentleman who was abroad. The name of the house would be Thornfield Hall. She drew its beautiful setting, its lawns and shrubberies, from Ellen's home, "The Rydings." But the house must be larger, more gloomy and mysterious. It must hide a secret and whisper the fact to anyone who came to live there.

Suddenly she remembered the battlements, the grim exterior, the dark rich furniture, of Norton Conyers, the house near Harrogate which she had visited with the Sidgwicks when she was a governess at Stonegappe. She heard the housekeeper's voice once again, saw her hand pointing to a heavily paneled door at the end of a passage, in a wing closed off from the rest of the house.

They say a mad lady was kept in there.

That must be the secret of Thornfield Hall!

Its owner would return unexpectedly from abroad. A dark, short man with an ugly face, a biting tongue and intelligent eyes. She fell in love with him as Jane did. She suffered, with her, the tortures of jealousy when he filled his grand house with fashionable guests and flirted with the elegant Blanche Ingram just to rouse and anger his little Jane. She encountered the enigmatic Grace Poole in the corridors of Thornfield. Her ears were filled, and her blood ran cold, with the peals of mad laughter coming from somewhere along the passage whose outer door Grace had, for once, forgotten to lock.

She felt Edward Rochester's arms about her that night in the garden when the evening star had risen and they had both declared their love and she had promised to marry him. It seemed to be she, not Jane, who dressed so carefully on her wedding morning. She, not Jane, who stood at the altar and heard the loud voice of the stranger who rose from the back of the church to call out: *The marriage cannot go on; I declare the existence of an impediment.*

And then—the secret of the locked room would at last be revealed.

But Jane must have her happiness in the end. She must! Jane, who fled that day from Thornfield Hall so that she might never again see the man she loved, must see him once more. The impediment must be removed. Removed terribly, perhaps by fire and death. But Jane and her lover had got to marry in the end, even though he would be maimed and half-blinded by the fire. For that sort of love does not go by appearances. It is real and lasting.

She pushed aside all Monsieur Héger's remembered words of advice. She did not even try to curb her mounting wings of imagination. She kept her feet on the ground only when she was describing her characters and how they spoke or thought. They were real people to her. She tried no longer to photograph life as she had done in *The Professor.* She painted, instead, a wild, stormy picture which lifted one into an unknown world. The world she was creating for herself.

CHAPTER *Twenty*

When the Haworth gig stopped at the parsonage gate once more, Arthur Nicholls was there. He sprang forward to help Mr. Brontë get down, but the old man proudly ignored his hand.

"Thank you, but I can now descend by myself. I see the step perfectly well."

It seemed a miracle to watch him, after all the time of increasing gropings and stumblings, walk steadily up the garden path. Charlotte did not disdain Arthur's hand. She clung to it slightly as she got down. Here was somebody strong and faithful, someone who guessed what she had been through, and who would always support her. The warm pressure of his hand told her that.

First Anne, then even Emily, threw their arms round their father's neck and kissed him. Martha watched jubilantly from the kitchen door. "Eh, but the Master can see like any o' us!" she exclaimed. Then the smell of the savory dish she was cooking for supper made her turn back hurriedly to the fire.

It was long before they could accustom themselves to the change, long before the sisters ceased to listen for the opening of the study door so that one of them might dart out and offer her arm. That first Sunday, the church was full to the doors. People watched their rector climb the steps to the pulpit without touching its wooden support. He could glance down at his notes as he preached. Arthur Nicholls need only read the Lessons now. As Charlotte sat listening to his voice she thought of the selfless dignity with which he accepted his old place as subordinate. Had the operation failed, he might have been in the pulpit instead. Or have gone elsewhere to a better income and a living of his own. She was beginning to guess why he did not.

Jane Eyre was half finished. All that winter she wrote steadily as the evenings darkened and the wind swept down from the moor again. With steady courage she parceled up *The Professor* and kept it going on its weary rounds. Anne and Emily had done the same with their books. They had almost given up hope of acceptance, but went on doggedly trying to sell them. But one morning Mr. Feathers, encountering Charlotte as she was on her way to shop in the village, handed her a letter.

"All t'way from Lunnon, Miss Charlotte."

She only said, "Thank you, Mr. Feathers," and walked on with it in her hand. He went on to deliver some mail to an outlying farm on the moor. She continued until she was sure he could no longer see her then turning into the nearest private spot, which was the graveyard, made hastily for a flat tomb she could sit on and read her letter.

One glance, as he handed it, had shown her the name "Bell." But now she saw it was addressed to "Messrs. Ellis and Acton Bell, %. Miss C. Brontë. The Parsonage. Haworth." She looked at the letter again. There was no mention, after all, of C. Bell. Hope died, though she tried to flog it into pleasure at the thought of her sisters' success. Anyway, she had no right to open the letter after all. The good news was to be Anne's and Emily's instead.

She went home and tried to look pleased and cheerful as she handed the letter over. Emily tore it open and read it, with Anne looking over her shoulder. They had sent both *Agnes Grey* and *Wuthering Heights* to the same publisher, a Mr. Newby in London. Now Mr. Newby wrote that he would be pleased to bring out the two books if the authors would make some contribution.

Emily folded the communication a little angrily. "But we'd decided not to put one penny more to the printing of our new books!"

Anne said nothing. But Charlotte, catching sight of her face in the mirror over the fireplace, saw the look of deep disappointment on it, followed by one of unusual determination.

Anne said, "No other publisher has been interested enough even to suggest it. He must be prepared to incur some expense himself. He must think *something* of our books to do that."

"I dare say he does. But not enough, evidently, to take the entire risk."

Anne still spoke firmly. "If you don't care to do so, Emily, I'm quite prepared to pay the whole amount myself."

Emily stared, then shrugged her shoulders. "You mustn't do that, of course. I see he wants to publish both our books together. I'm willing to pay my share."

Charlotte stood silent, for the first time in her life not the leader in this new project. After a few seconds she said quietly, "What do you want me to write, then, in reply?"

"Write that we accept his offer. I shall make out my check and Anne can do the same. You may enclose them in the letter."

Charlotte went up to her room and lifted the rosewood desk from the floor. But she stood with it in her hands a long time before she carried it downstairs again. She was fighting an unusual feeling, a feeling of which she was ashamed. Was it possible that she could be jealous of her own sisters?

She conquered it at last. Forced herself to say a few words of congratulation when she met them again, and to mean them, too. Then she wrote to Mr. Newby, saying that, as agent for the Messrs. Ellis and Acton Bell she was empowered to accept his offer and to enclose the amount he stipulated toward the costs of printing.

So the money Aunt Branwell had left them was dipped into once more.

She went on to finish *Jane Eyre*. She worked at it during the cold nights of that winter, when the snow lay thick on the window sill of the parlor, and the fire and the lamp burned bright. The year 1846 came to an end, with its memories of the stay in Manchester and Mr. Brontë's ordeal. The new year dawned and began at last to soften toward spring.

Charlotte had now packed up and sent off *The Professor* six times. Six times it had been returned with not a word of hope or encouragement to her, while Anne and Emily had been successful in placing their novels. But Mr. Newby seemed in no hurry to bring them out. So, while time hung heavily on the hands of the two younger sisters, Charlotte found herself so absorbed in her own new tale that she scarcely noticed it pass.

She heard, ringing out in her mind, Rochester's cry of "Jane! Jane!" calling her back to him in his agony and loneliness. She ran to him, and found that the tragedy which had engulfed him had set them both free. She wound up the marvelous story on a note of tranquility. "My Edward and I, then, are happy."

She looked at the piles of notebooks before her and began copying out the manuscript as neatly and tidily as she could. She altered and corrected. She was so busy, she hardly realized that spring had come and gone, and that summer was here now. The lamp in the parlor wasn't needed any more. The evening light streamed brightly enough on the pages, and the summer air stole into the room from the window, now opened instead of being firmly closed.

Even the return of *The Professor* yet again did not disturb her. There was one more publisher who hadn't seen it yet. She was short of paper and string, so she just wrapped it up in the same paper, scored out the address of the last publishing office it had been to and wrote above it: Messrs. Smith and Elder, 65, Cornhill, London.

Then she went back to her copying and correcting. But it was mechanical work. The excitement of inventing the story of *Jane Eyre* was over. In between numbering her pages and rephrasing sentences she, too, began to feel the time long. Some weeks had elapsed since she had sent off the package. Surely Messrs. Smith and Elder could have replied by now?

She wrote them a letter. She said: "Gentlemen—About three weeks since I sent for your consideration a MS entitled *'The Professor,'* a tale by Currer Bell. I should be glad to know whether it reached your hands safely, and likewise to learn, at your earliest convenience, whether it be such as you can undertake to publish. I am, Gentlemen, yours respectfully, CURRER BELL.

She almost wished she had not written, when, after a few days, the well-worn package came back to her hands. Perhaps she should have let them have longer time to consider? Perhaps she had hurried them too much and they had not had time even to read *The Professor.* Perhaps . . .

Anyway, it had come back again. She thought she knew already what the letter enclosed with it would say. But it did seem longer than usual. She trembled a little as she read it. It was a refusal, certainly, but phrased so kindly that its very wording gave comfort. It held out hope, too. For, though it said that the present work was too short and too lacking in interest, it showed enough talent for the publishers to wish to read anything more from Currer Bell's pen, especially if it were longer.

She sat down immediately and wrote to Smith and Elder again. She thanked them gratefully for their words of encouragement. She said that she had almost completed a new novel, which had more action and variety in it. Might she send it to them?

Then she went back to her task of correction and polishing, this time with a tiny hope in her heart. The manuscript of the book lay now, copied out, clear and legible in her own meticulous handwriting. She faced it with a clean sheet of paper and wrote: JANE EYRE. A tale by CURRER BELL.

She parceled it up, walked out to the little post office and started it on its long journey to London.

CHAPTER *Twenty-one*

Late summer of the year 1847. The trees in the London parks hung their heads, covered with dust. The gardens in the squares were dusty and drooping, too. They were empty as well since almost every London family of means had gone to the coast or the country to escape the heat.

The Royal Standard was lowered over Buckingham Palace. Her Majesty had followed her subjects and left the City. Hyde Park had lost its Sunday procession of carriages. The heart of London was almost stilled. It beat only in the business quarters, where clerks toiled with their jackets off and business gentlemen cursed the necessity of turning up at their offices in this heat.

Young Mr. Smith, of Smith and Elder, sat down at his desk one morning and looked distastefully at the pile of correspondence awaiting his attention. The list of publications for autumn was nearly completed. Thank heaven for that! Several new manuscripts had arrived that morning. He stared at them wearily, reluctant even to open them. His chief reader, Mr. Williams, had already taken a batch home to read yesterday. Should they contain anything worth publishing, then this new lot could wait. They couldn't be brought out this year anyway.

He picked up a silver paper knife and began opening his letters. He had scarcely read the first through, when the door opened behind him. He knew who it was. Without looking up he said, "Good morning, Mr. Williams. No masterpiece among yesterday's lot I suppose?"

"I'm not so sure about that. There's one here that claimed my attention. In fact I could scarcely put it down."

Mr. Smith received the news with a pale smile. William Smith Williams had but one fault. He was apt to see geese as swans. His "I could scarcely put it down" had sometimes heralded quite a mediocre book. Mr. Smith was not much impressed.

"What's it called?"

"*Jane Eyre*. By a writer who calls himself Currer Bell."

"An unknown novelist doesn't have much in the way of sales. We shouldn't risk it, you know."

"Perhaps we should risk it in this case. I assure you, I've seldom been so moved and excited by anything. This book, *Jane Eyre,* is an extraordinary production! It has a fascinating plot. Its characters are so odd and unusual! It quite sweeps one along——"

George Smith smiled again. "I can see it has swept *you* along! Have you brought it with you?"

"Here it is."

"Thanks. I'll look at it myself when I've a moment."

When the other had left the room, George Smith sat staring at the manuscript for a moment. The writing was clear but very small. His eyes were tired already with reading so many manuscripts at home. Williams' enthusiasm sounded ridiculous. He would only be in for another disappointment, with the added embarrassment of telling his reader that he had been mistaken. If only the fellow would keep a cool head and remember production costs!

An idea struck him suddenly. He got up and rang the bell. When a clerk answered it, he said, "Please ask Mr. Taylor to see me for a moment."

James Taylor stepped into the room, a red-haired Scot who was extremely hardheaded and unimpressionable. The last person belonging to the firm, in fact, to let himself be "carried away."

"Look, Mr. Taylor. Here's the manuscript of a new novel which seems to have stirred Mr. Williams' interest." He paused as he handed it over. His eyes twinkled as he added, "You know how easily that is aroused."

The other nodded. "Yes, so it is."

"Now, you're levelheaded enough. Will you take it home tonight and give me a report in the morning?"

"All right, if you want me to."

James Taylor bundled the manuscript casually under his arm as if it were grocers' merchandise. At the door he turned to remark, "I'm not so easily swept off *my* feet!" then vanished.

George Smith returned to his desk and got on with the day's work. Both it, and the heat, so exhausted him that by the time he went home at night he had forgotten about the new book. Next morning, however, he was forced to remember it. He was a little late in reaching his office, and when he entered his room, Mr. Taylor was there already. This was most unusual.

"Good morning. Nothing terrible happened, I suppose?"

Taylor had placed the manuscript down on the desk.

Now he touched it reverently. Not casually, as of yesterday.

"Nothing terrible. But—you remember that novel you gave me to read last night? *Jane Eyre?*"

"Oh, yes. The one Williams praised so. What about it?"

"What about it?" The little Scot was beside himself with excitement. "I started reading it and I couldn't stop! I tell you, I read it half through the night! And the other half of the night I couldn't sleep. I just couldn't sleep for thinking about it! It's—it's a work of genius I tell you. That's what it is!"

His employer cast a sharp glance at him. Had Mr. Taylor by any chance been making a night of it? Was the fellow drunk? No, he didn't seem to be. Unless one can be drunk with enthusiasm. So there must be something special about the book after all.

"Thank you," he said after a pause. "I'll take it home tonight and read it myself."

George Smith's home was in Paddington. Not the Paddington of today, but a pleasant district of quiet garden squares; of handsome pillared houses with carriage steps in front of their doors so that the female occupants need not soil their long, crinolined skirts by stepping down from their carriages into the gutter. He lived at Number 4, Westbourne Place. His widowed mother kept house for him there, running the house in opulent comfort, as befitted a rising young publisher.

He arrived back home in the cool of the evening. The dusty trees outlined themselves against a bronze sky that promised a thunderstorm later on. Even the delicious dinner planned by Mrs. Smith to refresh him did not make him feel any more inclined for work in the evening. Tomorrow was Sunday. He would glance at *Jane Eyre* after breakfast, before driving to church with his mother. An hour, half an hour even, would be quite long enough to tell him whether the book really had quality or not.

The thunderstorm came in the night. The air felt fresher next morning. He felt a little more disposed to sample *Jane Eyre* after breakfast. So he withdrew to his handsome library at the back of the house and began the first sentence on the first page:

There was no possibility of taking a walk that day. . . .

At a quarter to eleven his mother looked in.

"George, the carriage is at the door. We shall be late for church!"

She had to speak twice before he even looked up. When he did, it was to say absently, "I'm sorry Mama. I'm not going out this morning."

The carriage went off and returned. Mrs. Smith had ordered a delicious cold soup, salmon in mayonnaise and an ice pudding for lunch. But when a servant was sent to call him, he only looked annoyed at the interruption.

"You can bring me some sandwiches and a glass of wine. I'm too busy to come to lunch."

He didn't even want any tea. The suggestion of a tray in the library was refused curtly. By dinnertime, his mother and one of the two sisters who lived with them, had become quite alarmed. They both invaded the library and forcibly dragged him to dinner. During the meal he scarcely spoke. They could see his mind was very far away. It had in fact, left Westbourne Place altogether. It was at Thornfield Hall with Jane.

Next morning he came to the office a new man, with a brisk step and a light in his eye. He sent for both Mr.

Williams and Mr. Taylor. "Gentlemen," he began, "you were perfectly right. This is an astonishing book. It will make the name of Currer Bell known from one end of England to the other."

James Taylor only nodded his head in agreement. But Mr. Williams was jubilant. "I thought you would say so! I was sure you would agree with my verdict!"

Mr. Taylor brought them both down to earth. "When do you plan to bring it out?" he demanded.

"It must come out immediately! Without delay! We must hurry the printers, get the advance publicity in hand. We must bring it out, if possible, in a month."

"Always supposing this fellow, Currer Bell is willing——" Mr. Taylor put in cautiously.

"He'll be willing enough when he gets my offer."

He sat down at his desk, disregarding them, and began to write his letter to Currer Bell. The office boy took it to the post, making a special journey so that the letter could travel up to the wilds of Yorkshire (where *was* Haworth anyway?) and reach the unknown author with as little time wasted as possible.

The big thunderstorm seemed to travel up north with it. It reached Haworth before the letter did. It roared and crashed over the moor and shook the windows of the parsonage, keeping Anne—who was afraid of thunderstorms—awake nearly all night. Then it cleared away in the early hours of the morning. The brooding heat which had hung over the village was gone. The air felt sparkling and fresh.

Today Anne and Emily had to skimp their morning tasks, for at last the proofs of their books had arrived from Newby, the publisher, who intended to bring out both

Wuthering Heights and *Agnes Grey* the next month. They sat down immediately after breakfast to finish correcting them. They had been at work on the proofs for nearly a week now. It was a tiresome, though thrilling, task.

Charlotte watched them at it a little sadly. How much she would have loved to be doing the same thing! Then she went to get a clean duster from Martha, and ran upstairs to dust Papa's room, a duty generally undertaken by Anne.

She dusted and swept and tidied till post time. She did not expect any mail this morning. *Jane Eyre* had only been dispatched a few days ago. The package (she could scarcely hope, now, for anything more but its return) could not be expected quite yet. But she heard a step in the hall and looking over the banisters, saw Mr. Feathers, who had taken advantage of the open front door, laying a letter down on the chair beside it.

"Suthin' for you, Miss Charlotte!" he called up, seeing her shadow fall on the stair.

She ran down quickly and picked up the letter. The hall was cool and silent so she opened it there. It was from Messrs. Smith and Elder and was signed "George Smith." It said the Firm would be pleased to publish the book *Jane Eyre* by Currer Bell, if Mr. Bell would agree to accept £500.

Accept, not pay this time! Accept £500. But the money wasn't the only thing. It wasn't the chief thing at all. Somebody wanted her book. She was to be an author at last.

All of a sudden, she had to lean against the wall, while tears of joy coursed down her cheeks. She felt almost faint with happiness.

CHAPTER *Twenty-two*

So, in that autumn, the novels of the three sisters came out almost together.

The gentle romance of *Agnes Grey* had very little success. The wild, supernatural tale of *Wuthering Heights* attracted more attention, but not all of it was flattering. One or two critics hailed it as something quite out of the common. Most of them found it "coarse" and wondered how any man could have written such a book.

Emily said nothing, but she was deeply hurt. No one could find anything coarse in the book now, any more than she did then. But she had put down thoughts and feelings too strong and real for the novel-reading public of the day. If that public had dreamed that a woman had written the book, it would have held up its collective hands in horror. However, the secret of the authors' identities was safely kept. Charlotte wrote all the business letters as "agent" for Ellis, Acton, and Currer Bell. Even Mr. Smith did not know that Charlotte Brontë herself was Currer Bell.

And *Jane Eyre?*

Soon the whole English-speaking world was reading

it. America raved over it, too. No one could tear themselves away from the adventures of the plain little governess and her master. Everyone in London was losing sleep over it. Plump little Queen Victoria snatched time from her endless signing of State Papers to devour it breathlessly. How could she guess that the writer had watched her pass by, during that summer in Brussels; a tiny woman like herself, elbowed about by the crowd while she rode by in her carriage? William Makepeace Thackeray read it and enthused over it at literary gatherings.

That season, both the famous and the unknown talked about nothing else. It traveled into the most distant parts of the country. Henry Nussey, who had put on weight now and was more pompous than ever, had to rebuke his rich wife for wasting her time "over a novel."

"But read it yourself, Henry! You will be fascinated, I assure you."

"Fascinated? Humph!" But he was interested enough to pick up the book after she had finished it. And he did not lay it down at once either. One of the characters interested him particularly; the good-looking clergyman, St. John Rivers. He thought complacently that this fellow, Rivers, was rather like himself. And like himself, he was actually refused in marriage by the plain, ordinary governess, Jane!

"Little fool! She did not know what a chance she refused!" Then, because this reflection brought to his mind Charlotte's own refusal, which still hurt his pride, he closed the book with a snap.

Away in a lush vale in Yorkshire, Mrs. Sidgwick sat in her drawing room reading *Jane Eyre*. She had ordered it only because everyone else seemed to be reading it. A comfortable fire burned in the grate, since it was November now. The footman had brought in the silver tea tray and set it beside her. But, though she had poured out her tea, she let it grow cold.

Presently, however, she stopped reading. For she had come upon something strangely familiar. On a sudden impulse she rose and, with rustling skirts went upstairs, along a passage, and opened the door of a large apartment seldom used and known as the Red Room. It was the one to which Charlotte had taken Ellen to lay off her bonnet. She advanced to the middle of it and looked about her. Then she reopened the book in her hand, where she had carefully placed a marker. It contained a description of the bedroom where Jane, as a child, had been locked in by her hard-hearted aunt:

A bed supported on massive pillars of mahogany, hung with curtains of deep red damask, stood out like a tabernacle in the centre, two large windows, with their blinds always drawn down, were half-shrouded in festoons and falls of similar drapery; the carpet was red; the table at the foot of the bed was covered with a crimson cloth; the walls were a soft fawn colour, with a blush of pink in it; the wardrobe, the toilet table, the chairs, were of darkly polished old mahogany. Out of these deep surrounding shades rose high and glared white, the piled mattresses and pillows of the bed, spread with a snowy Marseilles counterpane. Scarcely less prominent was an ample cushioned easy-chair near the head of the bed, also white, with a footstool before it, and looking, as I thought, like a pale throne.

So it did. But how, in the name of wonder, did this unknown writer, this Currer Bell, manage to describe the Red Room so exactly? Was he one of the gentlemen her husband sometimes brought home to dine and sleep the night? She tried to remember who had slept in the room. It was very little used.

She went downstairs again, still thinking, still uncomfortably astonished. The last person to come to her mind was the shy little governess who had been such a failure. She had forgotten her long ago.

In another part of Yorkshire, Ellen Nussey was reading the book, too. Although nothing in it was familiar to her, the mind of the author was. She remembered various phrases and opinions uttered by her great friend Charlotte. She knew Charlotte wrote. But everyone said Currer Bell was a man. Still, there were some descriptions, some passages that sounded feminine to her. Dare she write and ask Charlotte?

She owed her a letter anyway. She wouldn't ask outright, she would merely say how the book had entranced her, and then, very carefully, hint her suspicion that Currer Bell might after all, be a woman, and a woman she knew. She wrote a few lines, then put the end of the pen in her pretty mouth. She didn't want to make Charlotte angry. She would say, after all, that she had heard gossip. That was true enough. Everyone was gossiping about the unknown author as well as reading the book.

When her letter arrived at the parsonage, it did make Charlotte angry. Both angry and frightened. She had revealed too much of herself in *Jane Eyre* to want even her best friend to know she had written it.

She wrote a sharp letter in reply:

"I have given *no one* a right either to affirm, or to hint, in the most distant manner, that I was 'publishing'—(humbug!). Whoever has said it—if any one has, which I doubt

—is no friend of mine. Though twenty books were ascribed to me, I should own none. I scout the idea utterly. Whoever, after I have distinctly rejected the charge, urges it upon me, will do an unkind and an ill-bred thing. The most profound obscurity is infinitely preferable to vulgar notoriety; and that notoriety I neither seek nor will have."

She was satisfied that she had told no untruth. Should Ellen read the letter very carefully, she would see that her friend had not once said she did *not* write *Jane Eyre*. But Ellen's mind was not of the exacting sort that would scrutinize every word. She would take the letter just as it read.

All the same, Charlotte felt a pang of remorse as well as anger that her carefully guarded secret should even be guessed at. If Ellen ever discovered the truth, she would be deeply hurt. Well, it couldn't be helped. Charlotte meant every word she had written. Her flesh and blood cried out against what she called "vulgar notoriety."

She had not even told her own father. The girls knew now, but no one else in the family. Mr. Brontë had been told about the little volume of poems but nothing about the book the whole world was reading. Charlotte hesitated, then made up her mind. Ellen lived a very social life, with a large circle of friends. She could hardly be trusted not to let slip some word that would give the authorship of *Jane Eyre* away. But Papa was different. He lived the life of a recluse, seldom meeting anybody. She would—she must—tell him this very evening.

As soon as dusk fell, she went in to his study with a lighted lamp for him in her hand. He thanked her absently, his eyes on his book. But she lingered, until at last he looked up.

"Papa," she said, "I've been writing a book."

This did not surprise him. She had been scribbling ever since she was a child. He remarked, "Have you, my dear?" with his eyes still on the page before him.

"Yes; and I want you to read it."

Mr. Brontë knew well enough his daughters' small script. He had still to be careful of his sight. So he merely said, "I am afraid it will try my eyes too much."

Charlotte swallowed, then went on. "But it's not in manuscript. It's printed."

He laid the book down then and gazed at her with alarm. "My dear! You've never thought of the expense it will be! It will be almost sure to be a loss, for how can you get a book sold? No one knows you or your name."

"But, Papa, I don't think it will be a loss; if you will just let me read a review or two, and tell you more about it."

She had been standing with one hand behind her back. Now she withdrew it and he saw she was holding a sheaf of newspaper cuttings, folded into the covers of a book. She laid the fresh copy of *Jane Eyre* on his desk, then, curling up at his feet on the footstool, began to read the reviews in a clear, steady voice.

He listened in some bewilderment. The reviewers praised in the strongest language possible. Many of the reviews were signed, and signed by names which were famous. Could they possibly be talking about a book written by his Charlotte?

When she had finished, she rose. "I am leaving the book with you, Papa. Perhaps you will tell me later how you—how you like it."

She went back to the parlor and tried to occupy herself with mending some linen. What other people thought of *Jane Eyre* didn't matter half so much as what he thought.

Yet she knew that, however moved he might be by it, he would give little praise. Perhaps none at all. He was always a man of few words.

At last she heard his heavy footstep crossing the hall. He came in to the parlor, the book in his hand. He looked, not at her, but at the other two.

"Girls," he said, "do you know that Charlotte has been writing a book, and it is much better than likely?"

That was enough. It was high praise from her father. Impulsively she jumped up and kissed him. He patted her kindly on the shoulder, as one pats a child who has done something clever, then ambled back to his own room again.

Secluded in the parsonage like birds in a hidden nest, the three girls read all the speculations in the newspapers and magazines with glee. Who was Currer Bell? *They* knew the answer to that, though nobody else did! Everyone thought he must be a man. They thought the same about Ellis Bell. The force and boldness of the two books, *Wuthering Heights* and *Jane Eyre,* made most people sure of it.

And then—the girls began to catch a new note of gossip which came from the south. They stopped laughing. It was only a whisper as yet. Only an irresponsible guess. But—some people were wondering, could Ellis and Acton and Currer Bell be one and the same person?

There was no means of scotching the rumor except by betraying their secret. At all costs they must not do that! Besides, it *was* only a rumor. It would die down presently. So they ignored it, and went on with their work.

That is, Charlotte and Anne did. Emily had apparently said all she had to say through her poems and the novel *Wuthering Heights.* But Charlotte had now begun a new book. Like the first, it was to be called after its heroine, Shirley. It was a story of life round a Yorkshire mill; of the kind of people she knew. It was not at all like *Jane Eyre*.

Anne had already finished her second novel. It had been filling her mind while awaiting the publication of *Agnes Grey*. Perhaps that was why she had been so determined that the first book must come out somehow, so as to create interest for the second.

She was right. The names of the three authors Bell were now well known, chiefly because of Currer's success. When she offered *The Tenant of Wildfell Hall* to Mr. Newby, he did not mark time as he had before. He not only accepted it at once, but offered to pay for it, too. And he hurried it through the press as quickly as he possibly could, though of course the book was not Currer Bell's, only Acton's.

Or was it? Mr. Newby had heard a few rumors too.

Jane Eyre was now in its third edition in England. Long, encouraging letters came to the parsonage from the firm of Smith and Elder. Kindly letters that warmed Charlotte's heart and made her write back gratefully, signing her letters this time, Currer Bell. Mr. Smith sent her interesting new books to read. She felt he had become a friend.

It was now June of the year 1848. The happiest June the girls had ever known. They had gained success, and kept their privacy, too. They could enjoy their fame, so long as nobody knew it was theirs. Their shyness made it impossible for them to think without dread of meeting strangers and being fussed over. Here, they could still be just the Brontë girls. In London, the mysterious unknown . . .

They had money now, too. It made only a slight difference in their quiet way of living. Papa could have all the new books he wanted. The poverty-stricken around them were unobtrusively helped. Each of the sisters bought herself a new silk dress.

And then the blow fell.

CHAPTER *Twenty-three*

It fell on a warm day in July.

Charlotte had finished her morning tasks and was sitting sewing. She sang softly to herself as she did so. The window was open and presently she heard the creak of the gate as Mr. Feathers came slowly up to the door with the post.

Mr. Feathers was not a curious man. If it ever struck him to wonder why the parsonage got so much mail nowadays, he kept his wonderment to himself. But there was only one letter this morning. Seeing Charlotte at the parlor window, he came back and handed it to her over the sill.

"Mornin', Miss Charlotte. And a fair morning it is, too."

"Thank you, Mr. Feathers."

She recognized George Smith's handwriting on the outside. Still humming a little under her breath, she opened it and read it. She stared unbelievingly at the short, cool note. Its full meaning hardly penetrated for a second or two. When it did, she sped out of the room, rushed upstairs and sought out her sisters.

"Charlotte! What is the matter!" They gazed at her in astonishment.

"Read this!"

Emily took the letter from her and read it aloud. Mr. Smith had written that he was aware one of the Messrs. Bell had published a new novel, called *The Tenant of Wildfell Hall.* He wished it every success. A correspondent in America had informed him, however, that the book was being offered there for a very large sum, on the understanding (affirmed by Mr. Newby, the London publisher) that its author was Currer Bell. Mr. Newby had clearly intimated that, in his opinion, Ellis, Acton, and Currer Bell were one and the same person.

Mr. Smith went on to say that he could scarcely believe it. It would mean that the new book which Mr. Currer Bell had told him was in progress, was actually finished and had been offered to somebody else. Would Mr. Bell kindly let him know if that were the case?

Anne stood bewildered. Why should anyone think that Charlotte had written *her* book? Emily grasped the whole point of the letter and spoke first.

"Newby is trying to make a fortune out of Anne's novel," she said. "Yours, Charlotte, was a great success in America. If people there think *The Tenant of Wildfell Hall* is by the same person who wrote *Jane Eyre,* they will rush to buy it."

"Let me read the letter again," said Charlotte.

When she had finished, she looked at the other two. "It's quite clear that Mr. Smith believes, too, that there is only one of us. That one of us wrote all four books."

Anne burst out indignantly, "How *could* he think——"

"Why not? He knows nothing about us after all. Nothing about Currer Bell even. He's never seen any of us. He's only corresponded with me."

Emily said, "You must write and tell him the truth."

"I could," said Charlotte bitterly. "But would he believe me?"

Nobody said anything for a moment. Charlotte was thinking of Mr. Smith's unfailing kindness to her. Of how he had taken the risk of launching her, an unknown author. Naturally he had expected that kindness to be repaid by the offer of any other books she might write.

But this was not what distressed her most. It was Anne who put their feelings in words. "It's not the loss of my book that he minds so much, but he thinks we—you, Charlotte have been deceiving him."

"I know. We must show him he's wrong."

"But if you think it is no use writing——"

"I'm sure it's no use. He'll only believe when he sees for himself there are three of us."

"You would invite him here, then, to meet us?"

"I had not thought of that. Yes, perhaps I could. I—I had better ask Papa."

But her father no longer liked being disturbed by visitors. It was not good for his health to be disturbed at all. And greatly disturbed he would be if he knew about Mr. Smith's letter and the suspicions at which it hinted. No, that would not do. She went slowly downstairs again. She must tell somebody; ask someone's advice. Arthur Nicholls knew his rector's mind better than anyone else. Again she felt that strange wish to lean on him, to get some help from that silent, taciturn man.

Then she remembered. He was to be away all day, at

a series of meetings in Bradford. Her sense of sick disappointment made her pause in the hall in dismay. She looked toward the closed door of the study. But she did not go in. She could not face another ordeal just now. She went into the garden instead. Presently, as she walked up and down it, she grew calmer. She re-entered the house and went up to her sisters again.

"I have made up my mind what course to take," she told them. "It is the only one, though none of us will like it."

Anne looked apprehensive. "What must we do?"

"I've thought it all out. We can't ask him here after all. Apart from Papa's health, we couldn't possibly expect a busy man like Mr. Smith to leave everything and waste two days traveling back and forward between Haworth and London."

"But if you think it would be useless to write——"

"Quite useless. Why should he believe any letter from me when he thinks I haven't been truthful anyway? No, we must go to London ourselves."

Anne's mouth fell open. "Go to London?" she echoed faintly.

Charlotte looked impatiently at them. "Don't you see? If we *show* ourselves to him; if we each claim authorship of our own books, that's the only way to convince him that we are three, not one!"

Emily protested violently. "It's all very well for you to say 'go to London' like that! I hate the very thought of cities. I couldn't bear it!"

She looked suddenly like the hawk, Hero, when it was first brought home and put in a cage. Charlotte hesitated. Emily saw her advantage and pushed it home.

"Besides, we can't leave Papa alone like that. Somebody must stay and take care of him."

It was true. The old man was apt to grow melancholic if none of his daughters was near him. He liked to feel them about the house, even though he remained so much alone in his room.

Perhaps Anne's coming would be sufficient? Charlotte turned to her. "You will come with me, Anne?"

"Yes—if you think it really necessary."

"I do think it necessary. Why should Mr. Smith believe my word if I went alone? But you are the author of *Wildfell Hall*. You can tell him so."

"When should we go?"

Charlotte had considered that, too. "Now. Today," she said briskly. "If we catch the train from Keighley to Leeds we shall be in time for the London express. We must travel all night, but what does that matter? I want Mr. Smith to know the truth as quickly as possible."

There was an afternoon train from Keighley. Emily, glad to do anything rather than face London and strangers, went down to the village to see if the gig could be hired. She came back with the news that it was not available. Never mind. She had arranged with one of the villagers to take their trunk in a handcart to the station. Anne and Charlotte would have to walk.

"What shall I tell Papa when you're gone?" she asked.

"Tell him at teatime that I've had to see the publisher on a matter of urgent business. Say that Anne has gone with me for company."

They began to pack. They packed their possessions in one small trunk. Anne timidly suggested putting in her new silk dress, and, since Charlotte did not forbid her, she packed her sister's as well as her own. Anne had never been in any town bigger than York. But she was not quite so afraid as Emily. Nor quite so upset as Charlotte. As she was about to close the box she remembered Aunt Branwell's brooch. It was a little thing of seed pearls and it had been left to her.

She wouldn't wear it traveling, it might drop off in the train, but she tucked it carefully into one of her handkerchiefs. One might as well look one's best when going to London. It was a great adventure.

Mr. Brontë had his midday dinner alone on a tray in his study as usual. The girls ate a hurried meal in the parlor and then set off. It was four miles to Keighley, but they had walked it often. This time, however, they were cumbered by heavy traveling clothes, each with an extra cape to carry in which they could wrap themselves and try to sleep in the train.

Emily ran after them before they had gone very far. She dangled two small cushions, one in each hand. "You'd better take these," she told them abruptly. "No use being so uncomfortable that you can't sleep. You'll have to have your wits about you when you reach London."

The man with the handcart had started first. They saw him trudging along stolidly before them. It was a sultry day, with thunder in the air. Just as the smoke from the Keighley chimneys appeared on the horizon, the rain came down. Heavy, pelting thunder-rain. Anne put her cape right over her head. Charlotte trudged stolidly on, through the puddles that splashed her long skirts.

At Keighley, the little trunk stood on the platform already. They were glad to get into the train and to find an empty carriage where they could change some of their streaming garments and wipe the mud from their boots. Even Leeds station was an ordeal for both of them, especially Anne. But if the bustle and noise was so great here, what would it be like in London itself?

They dozed fitfully on the hard seats of the London train, thankful for Emily's cushions. The lamplight above their heads made everything seem unreal. Now and then the noise of a station would rouse them again. Presently the windows showed gray, then pink in the dawn. Anne looked out wonderingly upon lush meadows, green hedges, so unlike the stone dykes of the north. Charlotte, exhausted, still slept.

There were more houses now. More and more, built of neat red brick instead of gray stone. They had reached the suburbs of London. People were drawing up their blinds to salute the day. Now the train roared through a tunnel and then past great streets and buildings. It was slowing down, too. Anne leaned across toward Charlotte and shook her gently.

"Wake up, Charlotte. We are here!"

Charlotte woke up at once, made herself neat, smoothed her hair and put her head out of the window to call a porter. The noisy platform confused her almost as much as Anne. It seemed as if the whole world were streaming past, through a fog of smoke and soot.

A man with a bushy beard, wearing a porter's cap, saw her timid signal at last. He heaved down their trunk as though it had been a paper parcel. They followed him out of the carriage.

"Keb, Miss?"

What did that mean? The strange cockney accent bewildered them. Anne whispered, "I think he means, do we want a cab."

"Yes, please." In Yorkshire they called it a ca-ab. He put them into one. Its floor was covered with straw which scented the interior strongly. "Wot address?"

"Tell the driver to take us to the Chapter Coffee House, if you please."

Charlotte had spoken the words with great dignity. It was the only place she knew of where one could stay in London. Papa had taken her there for one night, when he started her on her journey to Brussels. She did not know that it was a place where only businessmen stayed as a rule, not women, and especially not women who came unescorted. Mr. Brontë himself had only gone there because he remembered it from his youth.

She caught the porter's stare. More than that, she saw the wink the cabman gave the other man as he leaned down from his box to catch the address. She tipped the porter icily, and then leaned back in the cab as it rattled off.

Anne said, "Charlotte, did you notice?"

"He's an ill-mannered person. Pay no attention."

Anne subsided. She had forgotten her tiredness. She looked eagerly out of the window as they rattled along. The young shopmen were taking the shutters of the shops down all along the route. How well dressed and dapper they seemed! It was amazing how much traffic there was already, at this early hour of the morning.

She touched Charlotte's sleeve. "Look Charlotte, a dancing bear! His master has just got up from the sidewalk and is leading him off. Poor creatures, perhaps they've had to sleep there all night!"

But Charlotte scarcely replied. She was deadly tired herself. All the planning and strain had been hers. She felt one of her bad headaches coming on, too. How on earth was she going to feel clearheaded enough to put her case properly before Mr. Smith?

The cab stopped in front of the Chapter Coffee House. It was a respectable old inn in the city, but the man who came out to take their trunk, stared, too, when he saw only two little ladies in old-fashioned country clothes step out of it.

A man was rubbing a duster over the dark wainscoting that paneled the hall. Charlotte, still very much on her dignity, asked if they could have a double-bedded room and some warm water to wash with, please. The man called a chambermaid who led them upstairs to a big, stuffy room. She threw open the windows. Instantly the roar of London's morning traffic came in along with the dusty air of the streets.

"But the bed looks comfortable," Anne said when she had gone, "and the sheets are quite clean. Look."

"Yes, I dare say it will do." Charlotte felt drained of energy now. Anne was already on her knees opening their trunk. She began to unpack, stowing their few belongings away in an enormous mahogany chest of drawers.

The chambermaid came back with two jugs of hot water. By the time they had washed and changed from their traveling clothes, even Charlotte began to feel better. They went downstairs again, where a delicious smell of coffee came out of the dining room to greet them. A few businessmen were seated at breakfast already; travelers for firms in the north or clerks employed in offices nearby. There were no other women in the room but themselves. But the interview before them so filled their thoughts, they scarcely noticed this nor were able to eat more than a few mouthfuls of the good, solid breakfast placed before them.

They intended to call at Mr. Smith's office in Cornhill immediately afterward. Charlotte had opened her bag several times to reassure herself that his letter to her was still there. It was the only proof she could show that she was, indeed, Currer Bell. After a very few minutes at table, they rose and asked the passing waiter how to get to the office.

"Corn'ill, Miss? Only 'alf a mile or so from 'ere. The hall porter will fetch you a keb."

He bustled off to call up the porter. But Charlotte scarcely needed Anne's frantic glance to stop him. "Thank you. If that is all the distance, we would prefer to walk."

They had not forgotten the impertinent look of the cabman bringing them here. Perhaps all London cabmen were impertinent? Anyhow, she and Anne would not risk such a thing again. So they left the Coffee House on foot and, clinging to each other, plunged into the crowded streets in search of Number 65, Cornhill.

Mr. Smith, of Smith and Elder, had reached it a little before them. He sat at his desk, looking through the morning's post. He was looking for a letter with the Haworth postmark; a letter from Currer Bell. But there was none.

Well, no doubt the fellow was ashamed of himself. Didn't know what to write. And yet his former letters had been so brilliant! Had given evidence of a mind as strong and unusual as the mind of the author of *Jane Eyre* . . .

If he *was* the author of *Jane*. Perhaps the real author was, indeed, this Acton Bell who had busily sold his book to another publisher! It was hard to have been deceived after all his, George Smith's, kindness. After all the interest and encouragement he had poured out upon this strange new talent! After all the——

His unhappy, disappointed thoughts were interrupted by a clerk sidling in and standing at his elbow.

"Well, what is it?" he asked sharply.

"Beg pardon, sir. Two ladies downstairs to see you."

"Who are they?"

"They didn't give their names."

George Smith's mood was a bitter one just now. "Then ask them," he told the clerk who promptly sidled out of the room once more.

He was back in a moment.

"They won't say who they are."

"How the deuce do they expect me to receive them then? Oh, well. Better show them up and get it over."

The door opened again to admit two little ladies in black. The one who advanced first, was so very small, she almost seemed like a child. He rose and bowed coldly.

"May I inquire your names, ladies? I do not usually receive visitors without an appointment."

The smaller visitor spoke in a voice scarcely above a whisper. "You are Mr. George Smith?"

He bowed again and stood waiting. How long were they going to take to state their business? This was a busy morning. It was Saturday. He had hoped to finish work early and get home soon to the cool comfort of Westbourne Place. But now he saw that the little lady, the one who had advanced first, was actually trembling with agitation. She did not seem able to speak. Instead, she was fumbling in her handbag. Was bringing out a letter. Was handing it to him.

He took it and looked at it. He could hardly believe

his eyes. For it was his own letter, addressed to Currer Bell, Esq. c/o. Miss Brontë, the Parsonage, Haworth. But how in the world had it come into the small hand holding it out to him now?

He turned the letter over and saw that it had been opened already. This was too much! That his own letter should have been opened by somebody else and brought back to him by a stranger!

"Madam," he said sternly, "where did you obtain this?"

"It was addressed to me. I am Currer Bell. This is my sister Acton Bell. The real author of *The Tenant of Wildfell Hall.*"

CHAPTER *Twenty-four*

It was afternoon before Anne and Charlotte were allowed to return to the Chapter Coffee House. When George Smith's first stunned amazement had passed off, he insisted upon introducing them to the two members of his staff who had reported so glowingly upon *Jane Eyre*. Mr. Williams and Mr. Taylor were summoned to his room. The secret was divulged to them. Their own amazement equaled his. Anyone less likely to have written a novel like that, could hardly be imagined.

Charlotte had stopped feeling agitated. Her kind Mr. Smith no longer doubted her word. "But," she said, fixing her large eyes earnestly on the men before her, "there really are three of us—three sisters. Our sister Emily preferred to remain at home. It was she who wrote *Wuthering Heights*. Neither Anne nor I."

They hastened to say they believed in the existence of Emily. Looking at the two small, plainly dressed sisters, listening to their country accents and then reminding themselves that these were, indeed, Currer and Acton Bell, they felt they could believe anything.

Some biscuits and wine were brought in. Charlotte,

who had scarcely touched her breakfast, felt revived after she had eaten a biscuit and drunk half a glass of wine. There were some business matters to see to; some business papers to sign. Anne sat quietly by the window, looking down on the busy scene outside Cornhill. When the last paper was looked through, the last point discussed, Mr. Smith said, "May I have the privilege of taking Messrs. Currer and Acton Bell out to lunch?"

He was wise enough not to take them to a large, fashionable place which might frighten them. He had his clerk call a cab, and they drove a short distance to one of the old city eating houses renowned for its quiet atmosphere and good food. The dining room was divided up by high wooden partitions of polished mahogany. This gave each party almost complete privacy. Charlotte and Anne were soon happy and at ease with so delightful a host.

Then he drove them back to the Chapter Coffee House. "No doubt you will be tired and glad of a rest," he said. "But I hope that by evening you will feel sufficiently refreshed to receive a call from my mother. I am quite sure she would wish the honor of knowing you."

As soon as they reached their own vast, dark room, the sisters realized how very, very tired they were. They took off their dresses, slipped on their cotton dressing gowns and lay down on top of the huge four-poster bed, pulling its crimson quilt over them for warmth.

It was quite late in the afternoon when they woke. The muffled roar of the traffic outside seemed to have died down a little. The sun had traveled round to the west and was shining now through the red serge curtains pulled over the window. A solemn light like the light from stained glass lay across the floor.

Anne yawned and opened her eyes. "What time is it, Charlotte?"

Charlotte fished from under the pillow her big silver watch with the large figures on its white china face. Her shortsighted eyes needed it.

"Nearly six o'clock! We must get up directly. Mrs. Smith may call any moment, and we must be dressed to receive her."

The girls sprang up, smoothed and tidied the bed, dressed themselves carefully, and then saw to it that the chairs in the room were arranged for visitors. There was no public sitting room downstairs, and they had not thought of hiring a private one. Anne had already hung up their best silk dresses to take out the folds. Charlotte slipped into hers.

"What a mercy you packed them after all! I didn't contemplate any callers or special occasions."

"I did." Anne seemed to be busily shaking out her handkerchiefs as if looking for something. "I knew things would happen as soon as you said who you were. Oh, here it is."

"Here is what?" Charlotte asked over her shoulder, looking at herself in the glass.

"Aunt Branwell's brooch. I want you to wear it."

"But you must wear it. She left it to you."

"Please, Charlotte! It is you that Mrs. Smith is really coming to see."

Anne's neat fingers were already pinning the brooch to Charlotte's collar. The dressing table was placed sideways by the window. As she did so, she looked down and saw a very fine carriage stop at the Coffee House door.

"Charlotte! I see Mr. Smith helping a lady out. It must be his mother. We're just dressed in time!"

The chambermaid knocked and asked if she could show Mrs. Smith up. The girls nodded, and presently a handsome, middle-aged woman came rustling into the room. Her face was kind and her manner was warm. When she threw back her cloak, they could see that she was in evening dress, her plump shoulders appearing out of a swathe of amber lace, while a diamond comb shone in her hair.

"My dears! What a shock you gave George this morning! Which of you is Currer Bell? . . . To think that you, you tiny creature, are the author of that amazing book. I cried my eyes out at some parts, I assure you."

Charlotte curtseyed but said nothing, which was her habit when she had nothing to say. Mrs. Smith, a little disconcerted at this Yorkshire way of receiving a compliment, turned to Anne next. Anne was a good deal prettier, and gentler-looking than Charlotte. What a pity *she* wasn't the genius!

"You are Acton Bell, I suppose? But your real name is Brontë I believe. I hope you like music, Miss Brontë?"

"Very much thank you, Madam." The abrupt intrusion of music into the conversation rather puzzled her. She ventured to say, "But why do you ask?"

"Because of the Opera, of course. We are going on to the Opera. Surely my son told you? He said you seemed quite agreeable to the idea."

Anne and Charlotte threw glances at one another. They now remembered simultaneously, a word or two being said about taking them to the Opera tonight. But they had been too tired and excited really to take it in. Now Anne looked hastily into the long glass mirror again. But nothing could turn her simple, high-necked dress, made by the village dressmaker, into a gown like Mrs. Smith's.

Mrs. Smith caught the look, and with her usual lavish kindness put her arm round Anne's waist. "What does it matter how you and your sister are dressed? You are traveling, everyone understands that. Besides, we have our own box, where you may be as private and secluded as you like!"

They began to go downstairs. Anne asked timidly what opera was being performed.

"*The Barber of Seville*. I think Rossini's music quite charming, don't you?"

Anne could not respond because she did not know the opera. But Charlotte did. Instantly a picture of the crowded Brussels Theatre came before her mind: the smart Brussels audience; the close, scented air; Madame Héger on one side of her prepared to be amused but not stirred or moved; and Monsieur Héger, his bright eyes already fixed on the curtain, ready to be swept away as much as she was.

"Do you know the opera, Charlotte?" Anne had asked her the question twice.

"Yes, I know it."

They were down in the entry now, being greeted by Mr. Smith, who looked very fine, with his top hat in his hand. His two sisters were agog to be presented to Currer and Acton Bell. One of them was to go the rest of the way in a hired cab with her brother, to leave room for the visitors in the carriage. Presently they all drove off.

Covent Garden in the evening, when a little color

still remained in the sky. Diamonds and furs and finery being set down at the famous portals. If the Brontës had only been a little less well-dressed than the others, they might have felt it, especially Anne. But those handsome creatures belonged to a different world. There could be no thought of competing. So Charlotte took Mr. Smith's arm and walked up the grand staircase with him quite composedly, as though she were making her way through a stream of rustling ghosts.

As for George Smith, he was not unaware of the curious glances that followed his little, dowdily dressed companion. But that only served to point the contrast between what she looked like, and what she was.

"Gad!" he said to himself, "if these people knew I had Jane Eyre, herself, on my arm!"

Here were the doors opening to the boxes. She and Anne entered what looked like a tiny room, upholstered in crimson velvet, furnished with gilded chairs. Mrs. Smith went at once to the front of the box and gestured to the Brontë girls to sit one on each side of her. But after a peep at the dazzling audience, they both shrank back, affrighted, until the gas was lowered in the big chandeliers, and the opera house was dimmed.

Then they leaned forward eagerly to watch the story of *The Barber of Seville*. There was a ballet, but the sisters privately thought such caperings ridiculous. The lights went up again at the interval, and George Smith took his opportunity to have a word or two with his distinguished author.

"You have nearly finished another novel for me, I hope?"

Charlotte nodded. After a second, she went on rather

timidly. "I—I should not grumble, but I still feel there is something in my first book, *The Professor,* which is perhaps worth preserving. You are still quite sure that you don't want it?"

"I am afraid it is much too short. But your picture of Brussels is uncommonly vivid, and there is much in the book that I liked. Why not use the material in some other form?"

"I never thought of that."

The new thought passed through her mind again even while the opera was in progress. The opera itself had revived her memories of Brussels, for only in Brussels had she ever seen one before. Brussels on the night of the Queen's visit, with the fiery flowers in the park and the illumined streets and the crowds. The Rue d'Isabelle, lying quiet under the moon. The closed carriage dashing past her, with Maria Miller's impertinent handkerchief fluttering out of the window.

But Maria Miller must have a new name. Something glamorous like—like Genevra. Genevra Fanshawe, that would suit her. And she, Charlotte, would be the heroine after all. The English governess here in Brussels to teach and be taught. Yet the real heroine would be Brussels itself. But one can't call a novel just that. Brussels. People might think of sprouts. No, the city must have a new name. *Ville*—something or other.

Villette.

She came to herself with a start as the curtain descended for the last time. The lights blazed up again. Everyone was rising, preparing to leave. Mr. Smith was already talking about plans for tomorrow. She had answered them she supposed. But she must ask Anne, later, what had been really arranged. She was still with the Hégers in Brussels.

Something was being said about taking them to church tomorrow, to hear a famous preacher. Mr. Williams, the reader for Smith and Elder, had petitioned for that honor. Then they were to dine with the Smiths, in Westbourne Place. The next day, Monday, they would see the Royal Academy and the National Gallery, and take tea with Mr. Williams and his family.

On Tuesday . . .

Here Charlotte came out of her dream to say firmly, "I'm sorry, but we go home on Tuesday. Don't we, Anne?"

They couldn't keep up the pace any longer than Tuesday anyway. The contrast between their quiet, monotonous life in the parsonage, and this constant glitter and amusement was too much to endure for more than a day or two, however enjoyable it might be.

As it was, they were not set down at the Chapter Coffee House until long after midnight. They had had practically no sleep the night before. The two sisters undressed with speed and presently lay side by side in the huge double bed. But they could not sleep. Excitement and overexhaustion kept them awake.

Anne spoke softly through the dark. "At home, they will have fallen asleep long ago. But Emily will know, even in her sleep, if it is a windy night on the moor or a calm one. Here one can scarcely tell."

"If it is calm, the owl will be hunting. And Keeper will growl as he always does when he hears it."

The sisters lay silent a moment, thinking themselves at home already. After a little Anne said, "What a great deal we shall have to tell them! You especially, Charlotte.

Or—no, you would never tell them all the compliments you've been paid. I shall have to do that."

"Now that the secret's out I shall have to write and tell Ellen."

"I mean to write down everything in a letter to Branwell as soon as we get home. Poor Branwell. He wanted so much to be a successful painter. He was sure he was going to be famous. And yet . . ."

They lay quiet again. Then Charlotte said, "Don't say too much to Branwell, Anne, please. I mean about our success. Perhaps he was a little too sure. Perhaps that was the trouble."

Anne assented by her silence. But Charlotte knew that her sister was not asleep. That something else was now filling her thoughts. "What are you thinking about?" She asked after a minute or two.

Anne's answer was very surprising. "About Edward Rochester."

Now why should Anne, who had read the book long ago, lie there suddenly thinking about Jane Eyre's passionate, strong-willed hero? "About Edward Rochester?" She was startled.

"Yes. I was just thinking, Charlotte, how very uncomfortable it would be to be married to him."

Charlotte gave a little laugh. "Jane Eyre didn't think so."

"Perhaps not. I was thinking about—other people."

"Other people? What do you mean?"

"People like—you or me for instance. Edward Rochester might be a very romantic figure for a young girl to imagine. But think about living with him, Charlotte! All those explosions and ragings and teasings; even teasings can get to be too much sometimes."

"Perhaps." Charlotte was beginning to feel a little sleepy now. But Anne's next words jerked her wide awake, they were so unexpected.

"Arthur Nicholls never gets into rages or teases too much. He would be a very kind person to live with. Don't you think so?"

What did she mean by that? Was it possible that Anne and Arthur Nicholls . . . A curious feeling stabbed through Charlotte, catching her breath so that she could not answer. But Anne was speaking again, anyway.

"And he loves you very much."

Charlotte's moment of self-revelation had left her throat dry. She managed to say, "Nonsense. He has never breathed a word of anything of the sort. . . ."

"Do you know why?" Anne's voice went on steadily through the dark. "Because you're famous and he thinks you beyond his reach. You—you must encourage him a little."

Charlotte tried to speak lightly, scornfully. "You know I would never dream of encouraging any man!"

"If you don't give him a little encouragement soon, he will go away. One can lose love in other ways besides—besides death."

So Anne *had* loved William Weightman! And she was trying her best to save Charlotte from losing, by neglect, what had been taken away from herself. The little figure beside Charlotte lay very still now. Pretending to be asleep, so as not to be forced to give away any more of its private feelings.

But Charlotte still lay wide awake in the darkness, thinking. She had never thought seriously about Arthur Nicholls before. She had a sudden, vivid picture of the small bunch of primroses laid anonymously on her plate that spring morning. She knew suddenly what it had meant.

A bell tolled suddenly over the city. ONE. TWO.

She had begun to doze again, but it startled her wide awake. The deep, solemn tone was like the *bourdon* of Sainte Gudule. Only a great church—a cathedral—could send out a note like that! Could it be from St. Paul's?

She slipped out of bed to see if the dome of St. Paul's was visible from their room. Behind her, Anne now slept in reality. She could hear the gentle breathing. She stole over to the window, drew the curtains back as quietly as possible, and looked out. A full moon was floating over the roofs opposite. The street down below was empty.

No, not quite empty. Some late wanderer was making his way home, walking so close to the side of the building that she could not see him unless she craned over the window. But she heard his footfalls, and his low, whistling tune. And she saw his shadow moving along the pavement, cast by the gas lamps along his route.

It seemed the shadow of a short, powerfully built man, and the whistled tune held a mocking note. It was the shadow Rochester would cast, the tune he would whistle. Confused with fatigue and sleeplessness, she had a sudden, mad impulse to lean over the sill and call down to him; to see if Rochester's face looked up.

The footsteps passed on and died away. The shadow vanished. She let the dream of Edward Rochester go, because Anne had shown her the patient reality of Arthur Nicholls. She turned away from the window again and tucked herself in beside Anne once more.

Perhaps Anne was right after all.

AFTERWORD

This being Charlotte Brontë's story and not her biography, I have taken a few liberties. Some minor happenings have been transposed in time, others omitted or invented. For example, Henry Nussey's proposal of marriage was not made during his sister's visit to the parsonage but a considerable time afterward. The wife he finally chose did not record her sensations on reading *Jane Eyre,* but it is hardly likely that she escaped doing so when all the world was reading it. And if Mrs. Sidgwick failed to be struck by the extraordinary likeness, in that book, to one of her rooms at Stonegappe, it would have been very strange.

There is no record of how Emily came by her dog, Keeper, so I have invented the one most likely. Wider liberties have perhaps been taken with the Brussels section. And yet those who knew Madame Héger's *pensionnat* as it was in Charlotte's time, have testified that, in *Villette* she described it most accurately. Is it too much to suppose that the ordeal of Lucy Snowe in trying to teach the insubordinate "big girls" of Class Four, was in reality Charlotte's? The agony endured and the manner of conquering it—and them—seemed to belong to Charlotte herself. I have ventured to describe it as hers.

The character of Ginevra Fanshawe in *Villette* has been recognized as that of an English girl, Maria Miller, who was at the *pensionnat* at the same time as Charlotte. There were many frivolous, light-minded girls there besides Maria, one or two of them English. Yet the pupil who identified Maria as the original of Ginevra did so without hesitation. Again, is it too much to suppose that Miss Maria must have indulged in some such escapade as Miss Ginevra?

Finally, I must apologize for leaving Anne, Emily, and Branwell so much in the background. Anyone who wishes to see what they looked like can do so in London's National Portrait Gallery. There hangs the picture which Branwell painted of his three sisters. But this is Charlotte's story. I have written it in the hope of awakening interest in a remarkable girl who wrote remarkable books.

BOOKS FOR FURTHER READING

Brontë, Anne. *Agnes Grey, The Tenant of Wildfell Hall.*
Brontë, Charlotte. *Jane Eyre, The Professor, Shirley, Villette.*
Brontë, Emily. *Wuthering Heights.*

DuMaurier, Daphne. *The Infernal World of Branwell Brontë.*

Gerin, Winifred. *Anne Brontë, a biography.*

Jarden, Mary Louise. *The Young Brontës.*

Spark, Muriel. *The Letters of the Brontës, a selection.*

ABOUT THE AUTHOR

Elisabeth Kyle was born in Ayr, Scotland, where she still lives. She was educated privately at home, and at a Quaker boarding school in York, England. Later she traveled extensively in Central Europe and the Balkans as a correspondent for the Manchester Guardian.

Miss Kyle began her literary career when she was in her teens, with short stories for children, published in various annuals. She is the author of a number of adult novels, and of more than twenty books for young people, published both in the United States and in England. She has four books on travel and politics to her credit, and has been published in major magazines, here and in her own country. Her short stories have been anthologized with those of Faulkner, Hemingway, and Saroyan, and her talents extend even to the theater. A play written by Elisabeth Kyle was produced in Scotland. *Girl with a Pen,* which shows the happier life of Charlotte Brontë, is the only work on the subject to obtain the approval of the President of the English Brontë society before publication.